Table of Contents

Section 1

continued

Section 2

Level **E**

FOCUS ON Reading Strategies

Perfection Learning®

Editorial Director: Susan C. Thies
Editor: Paula J. Reece
Writer: Susan Mills
Design Director: Randy Messer
Book Design: Deborah Bell, Deb Yoder
Cover Design: Michael A. Aspengren
Contributing Designers: Tobi Cunningham,
Emily J. Greazel, Michael Aspengren,
Brianne Osborn, Sue Bjork-Rush
Photo Research: Lisa Lorimor

Reviewers:

Kathryn Black
Language Program Specialist
Mesa Public Schools
Mesa, Arizona

Cindy Brunswick
Literacy Coordinator
Center for School Improvement
University of Chicago
Chicago, Illinois

L. Michelle Johnson, M.Ed.
Education Department
Washington College
Chestertown, Maryland

Jan Keese
K–12 Reading Facilitator
Ankeny Community Schools
Ankeny, Iowa

Photo Credits: p. 15 ©Bettman/CORBIS

Some images www.clipart.com; www.photos.com; Corel Professional Photos;
Dynamic Graphics Liquid Library; National Archives; Mike Aspengren; Bill Ersland;
Cait Gillespie: p. 30

For information, contact
Perfection Learning® Corporation
1000 North Second Avenue, P.O. Box 500
Logan, Iowa 51546-0500.
Phone: 1-800-831-4190
Fax: 1-800-543-2745
perfectionlearning.com

ISBN 0-7891-6152-4

2 3 4 5 6 BA 08 07 06 05 04

Lesson 1

Jackie Cochran:
First Lady of Aviation

• *Biography*

Heads Up You are about to read a biography titled "Jackie Cochran: First Lady of Aviation." Before you read the biography, it's important to understand the words and phrases in the title. Fill out the word magnets on this page and the next page. If you do not have any prior knowledge of one of the words or phrases, you may need to look it up in the dictionary or ask an adult. On the "spokes" of the magnets, write any other words or people that you know relate to the featured word or phrase.

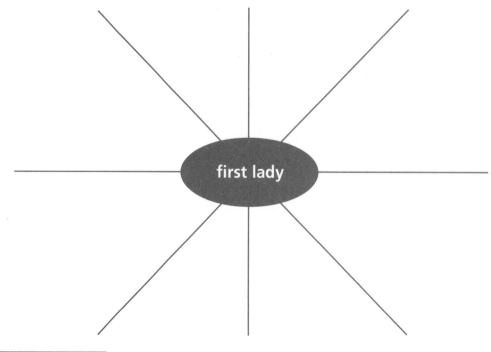

first lady

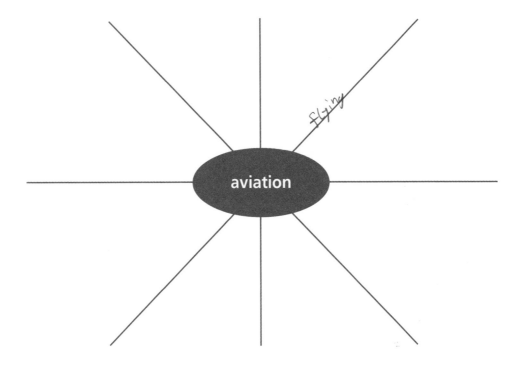

flying

aviation

Good readers are active readers. That means they ask themselves questions before, during, and after they read. They don't just passively receive the information. Learning how to be an *active questioner* will help you both understand and remember what you read.

As you read "Jackie Cochran: First Lady of Aviation," notice the Think-Along Questions throughout the text. By answering these questions in the "My Thoughts" column, you will be actively involved in understanding the text. Also, as you read, circle or highlight any words you don't know.

Jackie Cochran:
First Lady of Aviation

by Bonnie Highsmith Taylor

My Thoughts

1   Jackie Cochran once said, "Pity the man or woman who doesn't have the chance to love the way I loved flying."

2   For 40 years, she satisfied that love. When Jackie died in 1980 at the age of 69, she held more records in aviation for speed, altitude, and distance than any other flyer—man or woman.

3   At the age of 25, Jackie married Floyd Odlum. He was one of the ten richest men in the world. She herself became a millionaire from the cosmetic business she founded in 1935. She had come a long way from Sawdust Road, where she'd spent her childhood.

4   Sawdust Road was any poor part of a town. **What does this mean?** It was where the sawmill workers lived. The one-room shacks had no electricity or water. Some didn't even have windows. Jackie's Sawdust Road was in southern Florida.

5   When she was about six years old, she overheard a conversation between Mama and a neighbor.

6   "**Reckon** her folks will ever come back for her?" the neighbor asked.

7   Mama answered, "Don't reckon. It ain't easy. But I promised I'd bring her up. She's a burden I have to bear."

8   Jackie sat motionless behind the shed where she was hiding. She could hardly contain the joy she felt. She wasn't one of them!

9   Somehow, even at that early age, she felt different from her family. She felt as though she didn't belong.

10   Mama and the girls were unclean and lazy. Sometimes they'd go weeks without bathing or without even combing their hair.

11   Jackie had a thing about being clean, even when she was very small. Her family had no hot water. So every morning she would fill a tub with cold water and scrub herself.

12   "Mighty high and mighty, ain't she?" her foster sisters would sneer.

13   Jackie never owned a pair of shoes until she was eight years old. Most of the time she was hungry and cold.

14   Jackie's first attempt at an education failed. On the third day of school, the teacher tried to spank her. Jackie slapped the teacher. Then she bolted out the door and never went back.

My Thoughts

Why do you suppose Jackie's teacher tried to spank her?

15   The next year, Jackie heard there was a new teacher. She decided to give it a try.

16   Jackie loved Miss Boswick. If this teacher had stayed at the school, Jackie would gladly have gone every day. But two years later, Miss Boswick left Sawdust Road. Jackie gave up learning.

Who is your favorite teacher? Why?

17   When she was only eight, Jackie began doing housework and baby-sitting for the people in the mill town. But her foster mother took all the money she earned.

continued

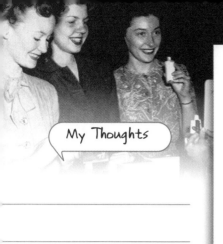

My Thoughts

18   Next, Jackie went to work in a cotton mill. When she was ten, she was made supervisor over 15 other children.

> Why do you think Jackie was made supervisor?

19   When she was 20, Jackie went to work for a high-class hair stylist in New York City. As her list of wealthy customers grew, so did her bank account. Jackie Cochran was on her way up. She had left Sawdust Road behind her forever.

20   Through the sales of cosmetics, Jackie met a lot of interesting people. It was at a dinner party that she met her future husband, Floyd Odlum. She confided in him her dream to have her own cosmetic business and travel all over the country selling.

21   Jokingly, Floyd said, "Then you better get some wings." It was no joke to Jackie.

22   Not long afterward, Jackie began a three-week vacation. The first day, Jackie went to the Roosevelt Field Flying School. She asked an instructor, "I'd like to learn to fly a plane. How long will it take to get a license?"

23   The pilot was Husky Lewellyn. He answered, "About two months, maybe three."

24   "I don't have that much time," Jackie said impatiently. "I only have three weeks."

25   "I'm afraid that's not enough time," smiled the pilot. "No one can earn a license in three weeks."

26   Jackie answered, "I can."

27   Jackie began her first lesson. No sooner had the plane left the ground than Jackie's heart began beating wildly. It was not from fear but excitement.

Never had she felt this way. Flying was in her blood. And it would be for the rest of her life.

28   In less than three weeks, Jackie had her license. She didn't know the difference between a biplane and a monoplane. She couldn't read a compass. But she had a license to fly!

29   In 1933, Jackie enrolled in a flying school in San Diego. She felt she needed more instruction. Jackie worried about the written tests she would have to take. She had so little education. Her writing and spelling were terrible.

30   The school let Jackie take the test orally. She passed the test with the highest possible rating. She got her commercial license.

31   Then Jackie heard about racing.

32   Jackie didn't win the first few races she entered. But it didn't discourage her. Jackie wanted to race. Nothing was going to stop her! Not even an unfair rule of the Bendix Cross-Country Race.

33   In 1935, Jackie tried to sign up for the Bendix Cross-Country Race. The people in charge said, "Sorry, this race is just for men."

34   Jackie was very angry. "Why?" she demanded.

35   The reason was ridiculous. In 1933, a female racer had been killed when her plane crashed.

36   Did these people think the same thing would happen to every woman pilot? And what if it happened to a man?

Do you think this rule was fair? Why or why not?

continued

My Thoughts

37   Jackie had an idea. She went to every man who was entered in the race. She asked them to sign a paper. It said that it was all right with them if she entered.

38   It worked. But Jackie had engine trouble halfway through the race. She had to drop out. But a friend, Amelia Earhart, entered and came in fifth.

What do you know about Amelia Earhart?

39   In 1937, Jackie won first place in the women's division of the Bendix Air Race and third place overall. In that year, she also won the Harmon Trophy as outstanding female pilot of the year.

40   She had set three major records:
- Women's national speed record,
- Women's world speed record, and
- New speed record of 4 hours, 12 minutes, 27 seconds from New York to Miami.

41   First Lady Eleanor Roosevelt made the presentation. During the years to come, Jackie won 14 more Harmon Trophies.

42   Jackie had many close calls over the years. Once the plane she was flying caught fire while she was at 12,000 feet. It was the one thing Jackie feared. She radioed the nearest airport to have fire-fighting equipment ready.

43   The heat in the plane was intense. The smoke was so thick that Jackie could hardly see the landing field. There was no time even to put the flaps down.

44   Seconds before the plane hit the ground, Jackie jumped out. The dry grass along the runway caught fire. All of her clothes and her case of cosmetics burned in the plane. But Jackie did not have one small burn. She did suffer an injury though. She broke her toe.

45   Before World War II, America delivered flying equipment to England. Jackie was the first woman to fly a bomber across the Atlantic.

46   She had an idea. Jackie discussed her plan with President Franklin Roosevelt. He approved.

47   So with 25 women pilots, she organized the WASPs (Women's Air Force Service Pilots). In 1945, Jackie received the Distinguished Service Medal for founding and directing the program.

48   Colonel Chuck Yeager was the first male pilot to fly faster than the speed of sound. Jackie Cochran was the first female pilot to do the same.

49   Jackie was still setting records when she was nearly 60 years old.

How would you describe Jackie?

50   How right Chuck Yeager was when he said, "Sometimes even Jackie Cochran couldn't believe what she had accomplished."

Make Sense of Words   When authors use conversations in their writing, they want their characters to sound real. This makes writing come alive. Sometimes the characters may use words or phrases that the reader is unfamiliar with or wouldn't use.

Active readers think about any unfamiliar word they read and try to substitute a more familiar word so that the sentence still makes sense. The word **reckon** is used twice in the conversation between Mama and her neighbor. Although this may not be a word you use, it does fit with the author's description of Jackie's foster family. In the sentences below, cross out the italicized word or phrase and write a word or phrase above it that will mean the same thing but that Jackie might have used after she left Sawdust Road far behind her.

"*Reckon* her folks will ever come back for her?"

"Don't *reckon*. It *ain't* easy," Mama answered.

"*Mighty high and mighty, ain't* she?" her foster sisters would sneer.

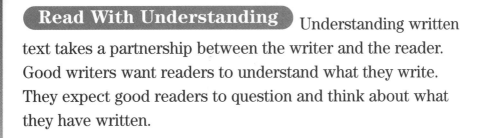

Read With Understanding Understanding written text takes a partnership between the writer and the reader. Good writers want readers to understand what they write. They expect good readers to question and think about what they have written.

Bonnie Highsmith Taylor chose the subtitle "First Lady of Aviation" because she thought it would give readers a good sense of what Jackie Cochran accomplished during her lifetime. She wanted you, the reader, to see Jackie in the same way she does. As an *active questioner*, you should think about the author's choice of words.

Which of the following is most likely the reason Bonnie Highsmith Taylor used the subtitle "First Lady of Aviation"?

① Jackie Cochran knew Eleanor Roosevelt, the president's wife.

② Jackie Cochran was the first female aviator to be so accomplished.

③ Jackie Cochran was rich because she married a millionaire.

④ Jackie Cochran would have made a good First Lady of the United States.

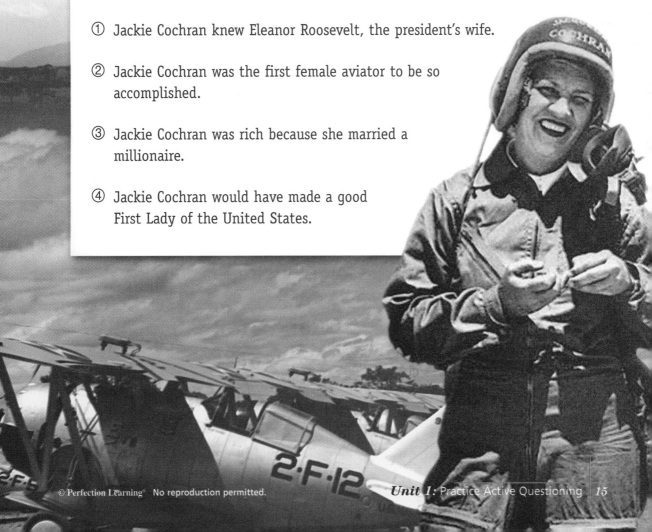

Understand by Seeing It An important question you, as an active reader, should have had in the back of your mind as you read this biography is "How did a girl from a poor foster family on Sawdust Road become the First Lady of Aviation"? To see how Jackie Cochran was able to go from a poor girl to a famous pilot, fill in the answers to the questions in the chart below and on the next page. You may refer back to the story to find the answers.

> ## Jackie Cochran:
> ## Foster Child of Poor Family on Sawdust Road

| **Question:** What did Jackie do to show that she was different from the rest of her foster family? | **Answer:** |

| **Question:** Why do you think Jackie was made a supervisor at the cotton mill when she was only ten? | **Answer:** |

Question: When did Jackie feel that she had left Sawdust Road behind forever?

Answer:

Question: How did Jackie earn her commercial pilot's license even though her writing and spelling skills were poor?

Answer:

Question: What three major flying records did Jackie set?

Answer:

Question: Why did Jackie Cochran receive the Distinguished Service Medal?

Answer:

Jackie Cochran:
First Lady of Aviation

Write to Learn As an *active questioner*, you should have questioned why the Bendix Cross-Country Race did not allow women to enter. Write a conversation between Jackie Cochran and the person in charge of the race. Write the questions Jackie would ask about being able to join the race and the answers you think the person in charge would give.

Lesson 2

Three Queens of Egypt

• *Online Magazine Article*

Heads Up You are about to read an article about three Egyptian queens from *National Geographic Kids* magazine at www.nationalgeographic.com. In the first two paragraphs, you learn that these three women were powerful in an age when men were usually in charge.

Good readers ask themselves questions before, during, and after they read. *Active questioners* often use the "5 Ws and H" that newspaper writers use to write their articles—*Who, What, When, Where, Why,* and *How.* A "How" question that you would hope to find answered in this article is "How did these women stay in power?" On the next page, write questions beginning with "Who," "What," "When," "Where," and "Why" that you would expect to have answered as you read.

continued

Who?

What?

When?

Where?

Why?

Active questioning means "talking" to yourself as you are reading. Active readers can do this in their heads or by writing. Think about the prereading questions that you have written as well as the Think-Along Questions in the text to understand how these women came to power and stayed in control. Also, as you read, circle or highlight any words you don't know.

Three Queens of Egypt

by Vicki León

1   Girls of ancient Egypt had it a lot better than most. By age 12, they could wear makeup. They walked their pet geese and played ball for fun. As women, they had rights not accepted elsewhere. They could buy and sell property, inherit stuff—even sue someone!

2   Still, men were usually in charge. But that didn't stop some women from defying tradition and taking over. Cleopatra, Hatshepsut, and Nefertiti were three outrageous queens who showed the ancient world what girl power was all about.

What does "girl power" mean to you?

Cleopatra: Political Party Girl
(Reign: 51 B.C. to 30 B.C.)

3   Mark Antony was fuming. The ruler of half the Roman empire waited impatiently for the queen of Egypt to arrive. She was late—on purpose. And when she finally **glittered** up the Cydnus River on a ship with silver oars, Cleopatra had the nerve to make him board her ship. How dare she?

4   Antony shouldn't have been surprised at the queen's bold behavior. Cleo had star power with the brains to match. Queen by 18, she had her hands full: bad harvests, a forced marriage to her brother, plots to overthrow her. (To fight back, she even ordered hits on some of her relatives!) Forced to flee her capital of Alexandria, she convinced powerful Roman leader Julius Caesar to help her regain control. But four years later Caesar was assassinated. Cleo was back to square one.

continued

Three Queens of Egypt continued

5   Enter Marc Antony. She needed his political support. He needed money. Rich party girl Cleo tempted him with excess by betting that she could blow a fortune on dinner. Intrigued, Antony watched as Cleo crushed a pearl earring into her now-priceless drink. That's all it took for the charmed yet greedy Antony to become hopelessly devoted to the queen. With his help, Cleopatra battled to keep Egypt out of the hands of her enemies. She lost. But instead of surrendering, she took her life—probably with the help of a poisonous snake.

How did Cleopatra probably die?

6   Cleopatra left few words. But Egyptologists think they may have found an order signed by the queen. On it, the busy ruler had scribbled: "Make it so."

Hatshepsut: Built to Last
(Reign: 1479 B.C. to 1458 B.C.)

7   Wearing the royal headdress, with a pharaoh's traditional fake beard on her chin, Hatshepsut was officially the "female king" of Egypt. Not bad for a girl who was forced to wed her 8-year-old half brother at 13.

Why do you think some Egyptians had to marry family members?

8   Now for action! Hatshepsut waged successful warfare against fierce invaders. She created a magnificent temple to the sun god, Amun. Organizing a five-ship expedition to faraway lands,

she brought ivory, ebony, gold, and trees to Egypt.
Trees? Egypt needed them to grow fragrant
incense, burned by the ton in the temple's
ceremonies.

9   To celebrate her 15th year of rule, Hat had two
100-foot obelisks erected. (They looked a lot like
the tall, narrow Washington Monument.) Getting
the granite for the structures down the Nile River
took a long barge, 27 boats, and 850 rowers!

10   Hat was an excellent ruler—so good that she kept
the pharaoh-to-be on the sidelines until she died. But
she lives on in spirit. In modern Egypt, Hatshepsut's
wonders, from an obelisk to an incense tree, are still
standing after nearly 3,500 years.

Nefertiti: Rebel with a Cause
(Reign: 1336 B.C. to 1334 B.C.)

11   Although Nefertiti translates as "the beautiful
one has come," Egyptologists hotly debate what
she really looked like. But this queen was more
than just a face.

12   Nefertiti co-ruled with her pharaoh-husband,
and they had big changes in mind. One day they
made a shocking proclamation that Egyptians
would now worship only one god.

How do you think this went over with the kingdom?

To honor the religion, the royal couple built a new
capital city called Akhetaten that was filled with
exciting new art and architecture.

continued

Three Queens of Egypt continued

13   Their world didn't last. When Tutankhamun (King Tut to us) became pharaoh, the new capital was abandoned.

What prior knowledge do you have of King Tut?

Though some of the art was rescued, gone was the one-god religion from the ancient world. In the modern world, though, Nefertiti remains a name—and a face—that won't soon be forgotten.

Make Sense of Words Good writers choose their words with care and purpose. Sometimes an author chooses a word not just for its meaning but also because it will add something to the reader's imagination. Through *active questioning*, you, as a strategic reader, will notice these interesting words and ask why the author selected them.

Read the following sentence from "Three Queens of Egypt."

"And when she finally **glittered** up on a ship with silver oars, Cleopatra had the nerve to make him board her ship."

As an active questioner, you should ask why the author chose **glittered** and not the more common verbs (action words) *rode* or *sailed*. Reread paragraph 3 of "Three Queens of Egypt." Then write below what you think the author was intending to show by using this unusual verb.

Read With Understanding In "Three Queens of Egypt," Vicki León chose subtitles for each of the three queens. Cleopatra is called "Political Party Girl," Hatshepsut's description is "Built to Last," and Nefertiti is dubbed "Rebel with a Cause." Ask yourself what these three women have in common. From the list of subtitles below, choose the one that you think would fit best with the article as a whole.

① Women Who Had No Say

② Women Whose Lives Had Happy Endings

③ Girl Power in Ancient Egypt

④ Girls Make Better Leaders Than Boys

Understand by Seeing It As a strategic reader, you think about similarities and differences as you read. These three Egyptian queens were the same in several ways. Yet, as an *active questioner*, you should also notice some differences.

Choose two queens from Cleopatra, Hatshepsut, and Nefertiti to compare and contrast. Ask yourself what similarities and differences there were between these two women. Then fill in the Venn diagram below. In the section where the circles overlap, write similarities. Write differences in the separate parts of the circles.

Write the names of the queens you chose on the lines beneath the circles.

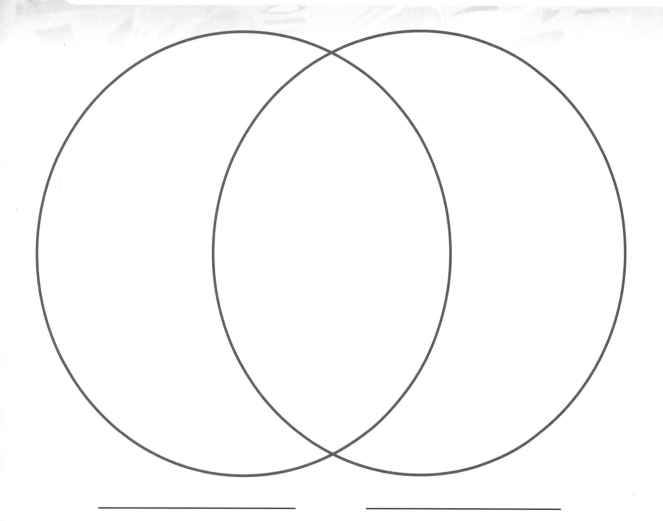

Write to Learn   Think about the similarities and the differences among these three queens. Ask yourself which one you would have liked to have as your ruler if you had been living during the time of Ancient Egypt. Why did you choose the one that you did? Write a paragraph explaining your choice.

Lesson 3

Alien Invasion

• *Magazine Article*

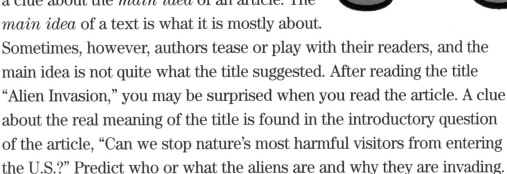

Heads Up Titles usually give readers a clue about the *main idea* of an article. The *main idea* of a text is what it is mostly about. Sometimes, however, authors tease or play with their readers, and the main idea is not quite what the title suggested. After reading the title "Alien Invasion," you may be surprised when you read the article. A clue about the real meaning of the title is found in the introductory question of the article, "Can we stop nature's most harmful visitors from entering the U.S.?" Predict who or what the aliens are and why they are invading.

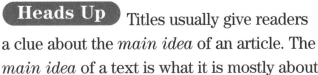

who is Alien,
Alien is from different counter

Respond to the Think-Along Questions to discover who the aliens are, why they are a problem, and if there are any possible solutions. Also, as you read, circle or highlight any words you don't know.

Alien Invasion

by Kathryn R. Hoffman

Can we stop nature's most harmful visitors from entering the U.S.?

1   This summer, the quiet town of Crofton, Maryland, was invaded by aliens. Townspeople swapped fearful stories of slippery, hungry predators that would eat anything they could fit in their jaws. Soon, the whole country was on the alert. The Bush administration promised to keep out the strange creatures. Said U.S. Interior Secretary Gail Norton: "These are like something from a bad horror movie."

What picture do you have in your head?

2   But this is no movie, and the aliens aren't from outer space. They were brought here by humans! This creepy tale is about a fish called the northern snakehead. It is from Southeast Asia, where it is seen as a harmless swamp fish. But in the U.S., the fish is an **invasive**, or alien, species. It is part of a growing threat to American ecosystems. Last month, Maryland wildlife officials poisoned the lake where snakeheads lived before the fish could do serious damage.

Who are the aliens in this article?

They Come by Air and Sea

3   Over the past 200 years, thousands of foreign plant and animal species have settled in the U.S. Most travel into the country with humans. Some nonnative species, such as a plant called kudzu, were brought here on purpose—for people's

gardens. Others, like the Asian long-horned beetle, slip in accidentally with cargo on boats or planes.

4   Some of these nonnative species have become **invasive**. This means that their introduction has caused environmental, economic or health problems in our country. Both kudzu and the Asian long-horned beetle have become problems. Kudzu vines smother trees and bushes. The Asian long-horned beetle turned up in Brooklyn, New York, six years ago and has since traveled to Chicago, Illinois. The wood-chomping beetles have killed thousands of healthy trees.

5   Many foreign species have no natural enemies in their new environment. This allows them to spread rapidly and threaten the survival of native species. "In eastern Africa, the [invasive] Nile perch has caused the extinction of 300 species of fish," says Guy McPherson, an ecologist at the University of Arizona. Scientists feared that the snakehead, which can flop from pond to pond across small pieces of land, would have a similar effect on U.S. waterways.

What is the problem in this article?

6   No one wants to keep out all foreign species. Many scientists are saying we should be more practical. Instead of trying to wipe out all foreign species, we should figure out which new creatures are desirable and which are undesirable. "Life would be easier if we could say native equals good and exotic is bad," says Mark Davis, an ecologist at Macalester College in St. Paul, Minnesota. "It's not that simple."

continued

The new fish have no enemies, so they start killing native fish

My Thoughts

7   Davis says that most nonnative species are harmless. Some are even beneficial to the environment. The European honeybee, for example, is important in agriculture. It provides pollination for valuable crops.

8   "But don't you wonder what the honeybee replaced?" asks McPherson. He says the European invader may have wiped out a native bee that did the same work. "We don't know what we're losing by introducing new species," he says.

A Balancing Act

9   Plants and animals do have a special place in their original environments. "Native species have a role in the ecosystem that they evolved into," says researcher Faith Campbell. "There's a balance."

10   The U.S. and other countries around the world are doing what they can to preserve this balance. Most wildlife officials agree that we may not be able to stop the invasions. But we can work to protect healthy native species from harmful foreign ones. Says Campbell: "We have a responsibility to take care of the environment where we live."

What are possible solutions to the problem?

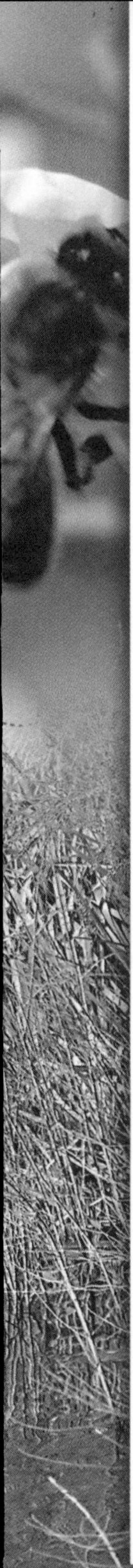

Make Sense of Words Sometimes authors will use a word that is important to the *main idea* but may not be familiar to you. The author often helps by using surrounding words as clues. These are called *context clues*. The clue may be a definition, an example, or an explanation in simpler language.

Find the word **invasive** in paragraph 2. Then find it again in paragraph 4. Notice that it is explained in the following sentence. Further help is given in the next few sentences by showing examples of **invasive** species. Fill in the chart below and on the next page to demonstrate your understanding of this word.

> "Some of these nonnative species have become **invasive**."

Text explanation of what **invasive** means

continued

Examples in text of **invasive** species

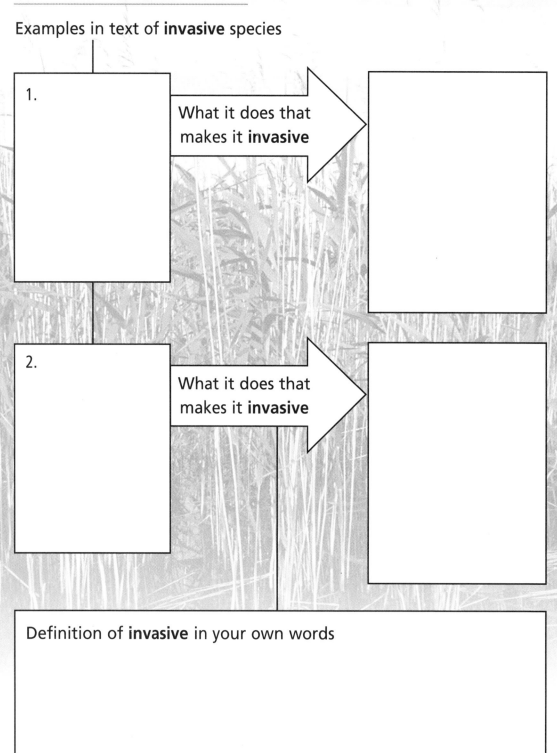

1.

What it does that
makes it **invasive**

2.

What it does that
makes it **invasive**

Definition of **invasive** in your own words

Now look back at any words that you circled in the story. Could you use
this technique to figure out what those words mean?

Read With Understanding Which of the following statements best supports the *main idea* of "Alien Invasion"?

① The European honeybee is important in agriculture.

② The northern snakehead is causing serious problems in the United States.

③ Most nonnative species are harmless.

④ The United States has no nonnative species.

Understand by Seeing It The *main idea* of the article "Alien Invasion" is centered around a problem. First, the problem is defined, followed by an explanation of what makes it a problem. Finally, possible solutions are presented. Fill in the chart below to demonstrate your understanding of the main idea of this article.

What is the problem?
Why is it a problem?
What are some possible solutions?

Write to Learn Imagine that you are a newspaper reporter. Use "Alien Invasion" for your headline and then write a one-paragraph article telling *who*, *what*, *when*, *where*, *why*, and *how* the "aliens" you just read about are invading.

Lesson 4

Dante's
Twelfth Birthday

• *Novel Excerpt*

Heads Up You are about to read part of a chapter called "Dante's Twelfth Birthday" from the novel *California Quake.* As you read, you will discover that Dante is excited about this special birthday. Pretend that you are turning 12 today. List special things you might expect to happen on this important day.

By paying attention to the Think-Along Questions, you will get to know Dante and understand the *main idea* of this selection. Also, as you read, circle or highlight any words you don't know.

Dante's Twelfth Birthday
from California Quake

by D. J. Arneson

1   Dante LaBella opened his eyes cautiously. He looked around his darkened room. His bed was shaking. It was rocking back and forth. Dante shook his head. Was he dreaming?

2   Beneath him, muffled by his thick mattress but still loud enough to hear, was a steady *squeak, squeak, squeak.* The springs were groaning. He'd heard the sound before. He knew what it meant. *Earthquake!* Instantly, he was wide awake.

3   Dante threw the covers off his shoulder. He opened his mouth to shout a warning to his family.

4   A firm hand gripped Dante by the shoulder.

5   "Sssh, Dante. You'll wake the whole city."

6   Dante blinked. A single candle flickered in the space between the floor and the ceiling. As his eyes grew accustomed to the half-light in the small room, he saw a hand holding the candle. It was his father's hand.

7   "Poppa?"

8   "Sssh. Who do you expect at this hour? Babbo Natale?" Dante's father grinned broadly. "This is April. Father Christmas doesn't come until December."

> Why do you think Dante's father called Father Christmas "Babbo Natale"?

continued

Dante's Twelfth Birthday continued

9   Giancarlo LaBella held the candle high. The room glowed. He was a big man. His shoulders were as broad as the back of the big, dark oak chair he had brought with him to America all the way from Italy. His arms were thick and strong. His legs were as sturdy as a horse's legs.

10   "You get dressed," Dante's father said. "Momma's cooking breakfast."

11   Dante sat on the edge of his bed rubbing his eyes. He grinned to himself as he watched his father's **husky** back vanish through the doorway. It hadn't been an earthquake shaking his bed. It had been his father. "No shaker today," he said quietly. He smiled. "Today is too special for shakers."

> Why do you think Dante thought the shaking was an earthquake?

12   Today was a special day. It was Dante's twelfth birthday. Today he would go to the produce market to work with his father. He was no longer a little boy. He was old enough to help.

13   Dante dressed quickly. He put on a fresh pair of pants and a crisply ironed shirt. He slipped his ankle-high boots over a clean pair of thick socks and laced them tightly. He rinsed his face with water from the pitcher on the dresser, which separated his half of the bedroom from the half used by his younger sister, Angelina. He rubbed his face dry with a clean-smelling, coarse towel. When he finished, he hung the towel back on its peg on the wall.

14   "Maybe I will get to drive the wagon," he thought to himself as he tiptoed out of the room. He closed the door behind him. "I'll ask Poppa after he's had his morning coffee." He walked to the stairs leading down to the first floor of the LaBellas' small but tidy wood frame house. Dante paused at the head of the stairs. "Maybe I better wait until we get to the market." He whispered, as if he were secretly planning a grand adventure with a friend. "Then he can't change his mind about taking me along."

> **When do you think this story takes place? Why?**

15   The day was too special to take any chances. Dante mustn't ask for too much. Dante made up his mind. He would be happy to do whatever job his father gave him.

16   Dante's mother turned from the coal-burning cook stove as Dante entered the kitchen. She put her hands to her cheeks and pursed her lips. Small tears came to her eyes, but the smile on her mouth told Dante they were tears of joy.

17   "Oh, my little Dante," she said as she crossed the kitchen toward him. She put out her arms to encircle him.

18   Dante **winced** as his mother hugged him tightly. He was already taller than she. Hugs were for little boys and little girls, like his sister Angelina. But Dante was twelve today.

continued

Dante's Twelfth Birthday continued

19   "You will be a man soon," she said as she patted Dante's dark curls. She wiped her eyes. Then she turned back to the stove.

Why do you suppose 12 is such a special age for boys in this story?

20   The stove was hot. A fresh scoop of shiny black coal from the scuttle alongside the big iron stove was catching fire inside. Bright flickers of yellow flame danced inside the firebox. The smoke shot up the metal stovepipe to curl into the sky from the brick chimney on the roof. Thousands of similar cooking fires were burning all over the city as night turned to day. People would be going to work soon. They had to eat. Today Dante was one of them. He was very proud. He sniffed at the bubbling pots. They filled the room with a delicious aroma.

21   "You may have coffee," Mrs. LaBella said with a smile at Dante.

22   Dante grinned. He went to his place at the table. It was next to his father's. A thick mug sat in front of Dante's plate. It was filled with steaming black coffee.

Why did Dante think it was special that he got coffee?

23   Dante watched his father lift his own mug to his mouth and blow across the top before he sipped. Dante did the same. He felt a pleasant warmth inside. He knew that today would be a very special day indeed.

Make Sense of Words When you come across a word you don't know in a text, first see if you can figure out its meaning by looking at the *context clues* given in the same sentence or surrounding sentences. You will often get enough clues to make an educated guess about the unknown word's meaning.

1. Find the word **husky** in paragraph 11.

   a. Who is **husky** describing?_____

   b. Now reread paragraph 9. After rereading it, you should be able to make an educated guess about the meaning of **husky**. Choose the best definition from the choices below.

   ① weak

   ② tiny

   ③ angry

   ④ powerful

2. Locate **winced** in paragraph 18. Reread paragraphs 18 and 19.

   a. Did Dante like being hugged by his mother? _____ yes _____ no

   b. Why or why not?

   c. Based on this, what do you think the word **winced** means?

Now look back at any words that you circled in the story. Could you use any of these techniques to figure out what those words mean?

Read With Understanding The *main idea* of "Dante's Twelfth Birthday" is based on the anticipation the boy feels for his special day. From the list below, choose the main reason Dante is excited about this particular birthday.

① Now he will no longer have to share a bedroom with his little sister.

② Now he can drink coffee with the grown-ups.

③ Now he can go to work with his father.

④ Now he will be able to go to Italy with his family.

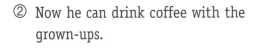

Understand by Seeing It Dante and his family see his twelfth birthday as a dividing line. This crossing over from childhood to adulthood fills his parents with pride and Dante with both pride and anticipation. Read the actions below that Dante might do. Decide if they are things that Dante would do before he turned 12 or after he turned 12. Then write the actions in the appropriate column in the chart.

Drive the wagon
Sleep late
Get hugged by his mother
Help his father at the market
Drink coffee
Play with his sister in the morning

Childhood	Twelfth Birthday	Adulthood

continued

Now write one sentence that describes the *main idea* of "Dante's Twelfth Birthday."

Write to Learn Pretend that you are Dante's little sister, Angelina. How would you feel about Dante's birthday? Perhaps you would be proud of him, or maybe you would be sad because you were going to lose a playmate. Write a journal entry below about how you, as Angelina, feel about your brother's big day.

_____

_____

_____

_____

_____

_____

_____

_____

_____

_____

_____

_____

_____

_____

_____

_____

_____

Lesson 5

Marconi and the Wonderful Wireless

• *Expository Nonfiction*

Heads Up You are about to read "Marconi and the Wonderful Wireless." You probably cannot imagine a world without computers, televisions, or radios. But without Guglielmo Marconi's invention, which enabled messages to be sent without wires, none of these modern technologies would have been possible. Marconi was able to invent the wireless at the young age of 23 because of certain things that happened to him and people who influenced him.

Think about your own life. Who has influenced you the most? Briefly describe that person on the next page and how he or she has helped make you the person that you are today.

Person Who Has Influenced Me

My mother has influenced me.

As you read about Marconi, think about what caused this man to become an inventor who changed the world at the young age of 23. Pay attention to the things that happened to him or to people who influenced him. The Think-Along Questions will help you recognize some of the *causes* resulting in the success of Marconi, the inventor. Also, as you read, circle or highlight any words you don't know.

Marconi and the Wonderful Wireless

by Shirley Jordan

1   Guglielmo Marconi was born in 1874. He was the son of a wealthy Italian father and a strong, opinionated Irish mother.

2   His mother took Marconi to England when he was three years old. They visited his older brother who was in school there. Once there, his mother placed young Guglielmo in a private English preschool. They did not return to Italy for three years.

3   Once back in Italy, 6-year-old Marconi faced a problem. He could speak almost no Italian. And what he did say was spoken with an English accent.

4   School was not a happy place for him. His Italian teachers had no patience with him. The boys at school teased him about the way he talked. He had few friends.

5   But Marconi had an inventive mind. He spent hours rigging up machines and experimenting with wires and batteries. He asked many questions of teachers and scientists.

Why did Marconi spend hours experimenting with wires and batteries?

6   Things improved for young Marconi when he was 13. His Italian had become better. Now no one teased him about the way he spoke. He had learned to sail a boat and had become a fine piano player.

7   His parents enrolled him in the Leghorn Technical Institute. There he had many chances to follow his interest in science. Soon he was studying physics and chemistry.

8   Electricity was a very exciting subject in those days. Marconi eagerly learned all he could. His mother saw this and paid for private lessons with well-known scientists.

Why was electricity an exciting subject in those days?

9   Something important happened during this time. A German scientist named Heinrich Hertz built a transmitter. It caused a spark to jump from one metal bar to another. And there was no wire between. His work with such electromagnetic waves was of great interest in Germany.

10   But there was no way for young Marconi in Italy to learn about the work of Hertz in Germany. Scientific papers and books were not widely available.

11   Marconi received a shock when it came time to think of college. He failed to pass the entrance tests for the well-regarded Bologna University. His mother knew many important people there. But she did not have the power to get him into the university.

What happened because Marconi failed the entrance tests for Bologna University?

12   She did, however, arrange for him to use the laboratories and library there. And she continued to find tutors for her son. One of these was a retired telegraph operator who taught him Morse code.

13   Marconi was vacationing in the Alps in 1894. He was at a location close to Germany. Hertz had just died. The newspapers had stories of his work with electromagnetic waves.

14   Marconi was fascinated with the idea of sending messages without wires. For days, he forgot his vacation and stayed in his room. All he wanted to do was think about sound waves.

continued

Marconi and the Wonderful Wireless continued

15   I believe I can make that idea work, he thought. Messages without wires!

16   Marconi returned to Italy. His mother cleared two large rooms on the top floor of their house. He turned to Italy's most famous expert on electromagnetic waves for help.

17   "I have failed to use such waves after trying for many years," Professor Righi told Marconi. "Why do you think a young man can do this? Especially one who has not gone to college."

18   But Marconi would not give up. He was determined to use Hertzian sound waves to send messages. He did not know that an Englishman named Oliver Lodge had already done this. But Lodge had lost interest. And he had not applied for a **patent**.

19   Marconi continued to work. Near the end of 1894, he called his mother into his workshop. She stood fascinated as he demonstrated his transmitter. He pressed a key at one end of the attic, and a buzzer sounded at the other end. There were no wires. Marconi's message had traveled 30 feet! Encouraged, he began to extend the distances for his experiments.

20   His father had often called Marconi "a useless son." But he was now interested in his son's work. He and his friends provided money for the wireless. Marconi's mother wrote her friends in England. That country was interested. Marconi and his mother sailed to London in February of 1896.

What caused Marconi's father to change his opinion of his son?

Handwritten note: because he was interested in his son's work.

21   Marconi at last applied for a **patent** in London. Then he began to work with the English Post Office. He planned a demonstration.

22   Marconi sent a message in Morse code for more than a mile. It traveled from one post office to another. Those watching were shocked. The message traveled without wires. And there were several tall buildings between the two post offices. They didn't even block the signal.

23   Larger and larger areas were used for demonstrations. Marconi demonstrated his invention for England's newspapers and the general public in December 1896. And in May 1897, he first showed how such messages could be sent over 8.7 miles of water.

24   Marconi became famous for the wireless. Now messages could travel where wires could not be used. For example, they could go from a ship to the shore.

25   His English backers set up a company, "The Wireless Telegraph and Signal Company." Marconi gave the company the rights to his **patent**. And he became a director. He also received 60 percent of the company shares and $25,000 in cash.

26   He had been working on his invention for three years. He was rich. Scientists all over the world knew of his work. And he was only 23 years old!

What happened because Marconi refused to give up?

He was rish.
His English backers
set up a Company.

27   The radios we use in our homes today are a form of Marconi's grand invention.

Unit 3: Recognize Cause and Effect | **53**

Make Sense of Words Sometimes an author assumes that you know a word and so doesn't define it within the text. It's then up to you to pick up clues throughout the text and figure out the word's meaning. The word **patent** is used several times in this essay, but it's never defined. Find where **patent** is bolded throughout the text. Then look for words or phrases that give you clues about the meaning of **patent**. Fill in the word web below with your clues.

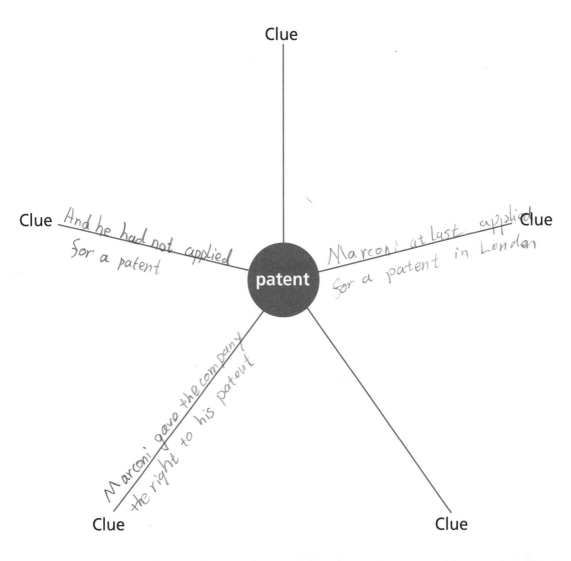

Clue

Clue _And he had not applied for a patent_

Clue _Marconi at last applied for a patent in London_

patent

Clue _Marconi gave the company the right to his patent_

Clue

After reading the word in the text and thinking about the clues, what do you think a **patent** is?

A patent is an official right to be the only person or company allowed to make or sell a new product for a certain period of time.

Look up **patent** in the dictionary and see if you were right.

Now look back at any words that you circled in the story. Could you use this technique to figure out what those words mean?

Read With Understanding Did thinking about the influences in Marconi's life help you understand why he was a successful inventor at the age of 23? Which of the following sentences below is *not* a cause of Marconi's success?

① Marconi's mother was a strong force in his life.

② Marconi had a great interest in electricity.

③ Marconi was able to build on what other scientists such as Hertz had done.

④ Marconi's father called him "a useless son."

Understand by Seeing It *Cause-and-effect* relationships are often found in expository nonfiction. In the organizer below, write the letter of the correct *effect* for each *cause* in "Marconi and the Wonderful Wireless."

Effects

Ⓐ School was not a happy place for 6-year-old Marconi.

Ⓑ Marconi learned Morse code.

Ⓒ Marconi was able to receive the first patent for the wireless.

Ⓓ Marconi was a rich man by the age of 23.

Causes	Effects
Oliver Lodge lost interest in using Hertzian sound waves to send messages.	
The young Marconi did not speak Italian very well.	
Marconi's English backers set up a company and gave him shares in it.	
Mrs. Marconi found tutors for her son, including a retired telegraph operator.	

Write to Learn Think about all the technology you use today that exists because messages can be sent without wires. Write a paragraph about the *effects* that Marconi's invention has on your life today.

Lesson 6

Those Three Wishes

• *Short Story*

Heads Up   You are about to read a short story called "Those Three Wishes." When one thing happens, like the granting of a wish, other things will happen afterward. You would expect the granting of three wishes to produce changes. The action or situation that will make a change happen is called the *cause*, and the change that results is called the *effect*. Many stories are built around these cause-and-effect relationships.

continued

Think about what you might wish for if you were given three wishes. What *effects* would your wishes have? Fill in the chart below to explore the effects of wishes.

Your wishes	Effects
1.	
2.	
3.	

As you read "Those Three Wishes," respond to the Think-Along Questions. Many will help you recognize the *causes* and *effects* that drive the action of the story. Also, as you read, circle or highlight any words you don't know.

Those Three Wishes

by Judith Gorog

1   No one ever said that Melinda Alice was nice. That wasn't the word used. No, she was clever, even witty. She was called—never to her face, however—Melinda Malice. Melinda Alice was clever and cruel. Her mother, when she thought about it at all, hoped Melinda would grow out of it. To her father, Melinda's very good grades mattered.

> Why do you think she's called "Melinda Malice"?

2   It was Melinda Alice, back in the eighth grade, who had labeled the shy, myopic new girl "Contamination" and was the first to pretend that anything or anyone touched by the new girl had to be cleaned, inoculated, or avoided. High school had merely given Melinda Alice greater scope for her talents.

3   The surprising thing about Melinda Alice was her power; no one trusted her, but no one avoided her either. She was always included, always in the middle. If you had seen her, pretty and witty, in the center of a group of students walking past your house, you'd have thought, "There goes a natural leader."

> Do you know anyone like Melinda Alice?

continued

Those Three Wishes continued

4   Melinda Alice had left for school early. She wanted to study alone in a quiet spot she had because there was going to be a big math test, and Melinda Alice was not prepared. That A mattered; so Melinda Alice walked to school alone, planning her studies. She didn't usually notice nature much, so she nearly stepped on a beautiful snail that was making its way across the sidewalk.

5   "Ugh. Yucky thing," thought Melinda Alice, then stopped. Not wanting to step on the snail accidentally was one thing, but now she lifted her shoe to crush it.

6   "Please don't," said the snail.

7   "Why not?" retorted Melinda Alice.

8   "I'll give you three wishes," replied the snail evenly.

What do you think will be the effect of Melinda's wishes?

9   "Agreed," said Melinda Alice. "My first wish is that my next," she paused a split second, "my next thousand wishes come true." She smiled triumphantly and opened her bag to take out a small notebook and pencil to keep track.

10   Melinda Alice was sure she heard the snail say, "What a clever girl," as it made it to the safety of an ivy bed beside the sidewalk.

11   During the rest of the walk to school, Melinda was occupied with wonderful ideas. She would have beautiful clothes. "Wish number two, that I will always be perfectly dressed," and she was just that. True, her new outfit was not a lot different from the one she had worn leaving the house, but that only meant Melinda Alice liked her own taste.

12   After thinking awhile, she wrote, "Wish number three. I wish for pierced ears and small gold earrings." Her father had not allowed Melinda to have pierced ears, but now she had them anyway. She felt her new earrings and shook her beautiful hair in delight. "I can have anything: stereo, tapes, TV, videodisc, moped, car, anything! All my life!" She hugged her books to herself in delight.

> Approximately when do you think this story was written? Why do you think so?

13   By the time she reached school, Melinda was almost an **altruist**; she could wish for peace. Then she wondered, "Is the snail that powerful?" She felt her ears, looked at her perfect blouse, skirt, jacket, shoes. "I could make ugly people beautiful, cure cripples . . ." She stopped. The wave of **altruism** had washed past. "I could pay people back who deserve it!" Melinda Alice looked at the school, at all the kids. She had an enormous sense of power. "They all have to do what *I* want now." She walked down the crowded halls to her locker. Melinda Alice could be sweet; she could be witty. She could—The bell rang for homeroom. Melinda Alice stashed her books, slammed the locker shut, and just made it to her seat.

> What caused Melinda Alice to feel powerful?

14   "Hey, Melinda Alice," whispered Fred. "You know that big math test next period?"

15   "Oh, no," grimaced Melinda Alice. Her thoughts raced; "That darn snail made me late, and I forgot to study."

16   "I'll blow it," she groaned aloud. "I wish I were dead."

    Unit 3: Recognize Cause and Effect | **63**

Make Sense of Words Sometimes an author will use different forms of the same word in a text. Look at the words **altruist** and **altruism** bolded in paragraph 13 of "Those Three Wishes." Each of the words has the same root but uses a different *suffix*, or ending, which changes the meaning of the words slightly. Use the *context clues* to fill in the organizer below about these two words.

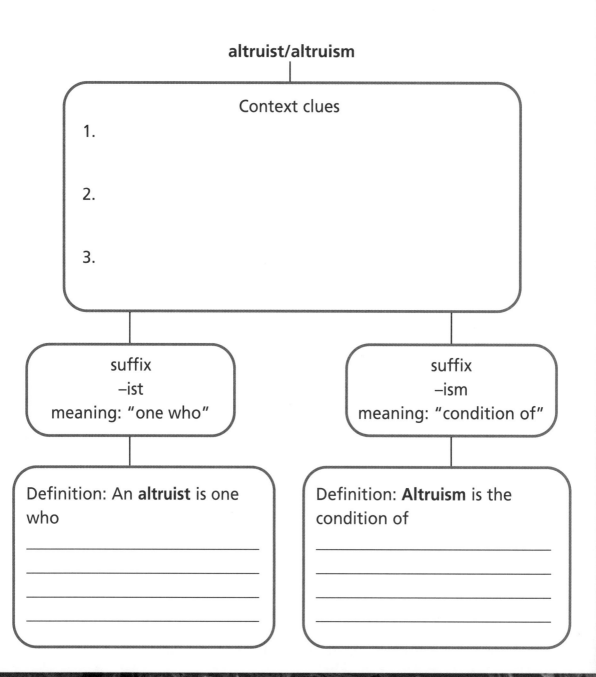

altruist/altruism

Context clues

1.

2.

3.

suffix
–ist
meaning: "one who"

suffix
–ism
meaning: "condition of"

Definition: An **altruist** is one who
_____
_____
_____
_____

Definition: **Altruism** is the condition of
_____
_____
_____
_____

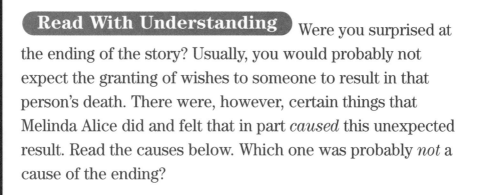

Read With Understanding Were you surprised at the ending of the story? Usually, you would probably not expect the granting of wishes to someone to result in that person's death. There were, however, certain things that Melinda Alice did and felt that in part *caused* this unexpected result. Read the causes below. Which one was probably *not* a cause of the ending?

① Melinda Alice thought she was very smart.

② Melinda Alice asked for pierced ears.

③ Melinda Alice had not studied for the math test.

④ Melinda Alice didn't think before she spoke.

Understand by Seeing It *Cause-and-effect* relationships are critical to the events in a story. Each different relationship builds on what happened before and connects one event with another. In the organizer below, write an *effect* for each *cause* that led to the next event in the story.

Because Melinda Alice lifted her foot to crush the snail, _____ _____ _____ _____

↓

Because Melinda Alice did not step on the snail, the snail_____ _____ _____ _____

↓

Because Melinda Alice thought she was very smart, she wished that _____ _____ _____

↓

Because Melinda Alice hadn't studied for her math test, she_____ _____ _____ _____

© Perfection Learning® No reproduction permitted.

Write to Learn Write a continuation of the story. Tell what happened to Melinda Alice and what happened to the snail.

The History of Counting

• *Magazine Article*

Heads Up The title of the article "The History of Counting" clearly lets you, the reader, know what this article is going to be about. What do you already know about the history of counting? What do you want to know? Write in the **K** and **W** boxes of the KWL organizer below and on the next page. After you read the article, come back to the organizer and fill out the **L** box.

> **K**
> **(What I Know about the history of counting)**
>
> _____
>
> _____
>
> _____
>
> _____

W
(What I Want to know about the history of counting)

_____

_____

_____

_____

L
(What I Learned about the history of counting)

_____

_____

_____

_____

Strategic readers think about what they already know about a topic before they begin reading so they can "hook" their new knowledge onto their old. In the previous units, you have been practicing other active reading strategies: *asking questions* as you read, determining the *main idea*, and understanding *cause and effect*. Respond to the Think-Along Questions as you read "The History of Counting" to gain additional practice with these skills. Also, as you read, circle or highlight any words you don't know.

The History of Counting

by Denise Schmandt-Besserat

My Thoughts

1   Most of us take our modern counting system for granted. We forget, or never seem to realize, that counting had to be invented and evolved over time.

2   The earliest counting devices are notched bones made by hunters and gatherers who lived about 15,000 years ago in what is now the Middle East. Although we don't know what these ancient people counted with the notched bones, these counting devices may tell us *how* they counted. Because each notch is similar to the next one and because there never seems to be a total indicated on the bones, it is likely that these people had not yet developed numbers. Each notch probably stood for "and one more."

What do you think the hunters and gatherers counted?

3   The counters found in the towns built by farmers between 5,000 and 10,000 years ago were small tokens of many shapes. Each token shape was used to count only one item. For example, sheep were counted with disks, but jars of oil were counted with egg-shaped tokens. (We know this because the signs for sheep and oil in early Sumerian writing pictured a disk and an egg shape.) This is known as *concrete* counting. The early farmers used the tokens by matching them with the number of things counted: one disk indicated one sheep, two disks two sheep, and so on.

4   The invention of *abstract* numbers was the real starting point of counting and is the one most of the world uses today. We separate, or abstract, the

idea of "one," "two," "three," and so on, from the thing we are counting. Abstract numbers are infinite (meaning endless) and can count anything.

5   We owe the invention of abstract numbers to the Sumerians who lived in the first cities, in the southern part of present-day Iraq, about 5,000 years ago.

6   For the first time, number and things counted were separated, or abstracted. Sheep and jars of oil were finally counted using the same numbers! The first farmers invented tokens because counting is important when the community depends on knowing things like how many bags of grain to keep for planting the next harvest.

7   Once abstract numbers were invented, they were used widely in trade and in calculations needed for everyday life. And with the greater use of numbers came the need for larger numbers.

> Why would a greater use of numbers create a need for larger numbers?

8   In the country of Sumer, the most common large number used in everyday life was 60. It was called "the big one," which suggests that, at some time, it had been the highest number.

9   While the Sumerians' system was remarkable for their time, it had one drawback: It had no zero. In other words, the Sumerians had no sign to indicate "no value." They just left a space. Doesn't that make reading numbers a bit difficult? Look at the number 204,501. How easy is it to read without the zeros—2 4,5 1?

continued

My Thoughts

My Thoughts

The History of Counting continued

10   The Sumerians' counting system was used for centuries. Why was such a complicated counting system used for so long? Perhaps it is easier to follow old ways of thinking than to come up with new ways.

Can you think of other examples of this?

11   But the Phoenicians, who invented the alphabet around 1500 B.C., came up with a new way. They used letters of their alphabet as numerals. By 500 B.C., the Greeks had borrowed the Phoenician system. The Greeks used 27 letters of their alphabet as numerals. The first nine letters were the numbers 1 through 9. The next nine letters were the tens, and the last nine letters were the hundreds. The last letter stood for 900.

12   By 200 B.C., the Romans improved on the system by reducing the number of signs to seven letters (I=1, V=5, X=10, L=50, C=100, D=500, M=1,000), what we call Roman numerals. Once again, common numerals didn't reach beyond 1,000, indicating how rarely large numbers were used in everyday life in Rome. Today, we still use Roman numerals for showing dates on buildings, for numbering volumes and chapters in books, and when indicating the hours on some clocks.

What is the main idea of paragraph 12?

13   But when we add, subtract, multiply, and divide, we use digits called Arabic numerals. And, of course, we write them as 0, 1, 2, 3, 4, 5, 6, 7, 8, and 9.

14   Where and when the Arabic numerals were invented is a mystery. Why then are the digits of our counting system called Arabic numerals? Because the Arabs brought them to Europe, around the year A.D. 1000, when they ruled Spain. The Arabs, however, called these digits Hindu numerals, because they had borrowed them from India.

15   It's hard to believe that for most of their time on Earth, humans had no numbers. How would our life today be different without counting? The list of ways is, well . . . **infinite**!

Read With Understanding Thinking about "The History of Counting," answer the following questions.

1. Which came first in the history of counting?

   Ⓐ Roman numerals

   Ⓑ notched bones

   Ⓒ tokens

   Ⓓ Arabic numerals

2. A word that means the same as **infinite** is

   Ⓐ *abstract.*

   Ⓑ *concrete.*

   Ⓒ *separate.*

   Ⓓ *endless.*

3. An effect of needing to know how many bags of grain to keep for planting was the invention of

   Ⓐ abstract numbers.

   Ⓑ tokens.

   Ⓒ writing.

   Ⓓ zero.

4. Why was the number 60 called "the big one" in Ancient Sumer?

   Ⓐ It was the age at which men could retire.

   Ⓑ It was the highest number.

   Ⓒ It was the age when most people died.

   Ⓓ It was the number of people in their Senate.

Now go back and fill in what you learned about the history of counting in the **L** box of the Heads Up section.

Understand by Seeing It The history of counting went from notches on bones to the system of abstract numbering used today. New civilizations added new ideas as people's counting needs became more complex. Fill in the chart below to demonstrate your understanding of the history of counting.

Hunters and gatherers counted by _____ _____.

↓

Early farmers used _____ _____.

↓

Sumerians invented _____ numbers, which meant that now anything could be counted.

↓

Phoenicians and Greeks used _____ as numbers.

↓

Romans reduced the number of signs to _____ letters.

↓

We use _____ numerals today.

continued

Now, after reviewing the events in the history of counting, write the *main idea* of the article in the box below.

Write to Learn The Sumerians' number system had no symbol for zero. Write a paragraph describing what *effect* it would have on life today if we didn't have a symbol for zero.

In the Dark

• *Short Story*

Listening comprehension is a valuable skill. Learning and practicing good listening skills will be helpful to you in your life inside and outside of school. When you listen, it is important to focus your attention on the speaker.

Listen as your teacher reads the story "In the Dark." Your teacher will stop about halfway through and ask you to make a prediction by answering the first question below.

1. Who can you predict is waiting?

   _____

After your teacher finishes reading "In the Dark," answer the second question below.

2. What was the surprise in the story?

   _____

   _____

Now your teacher will read "In the Dark" again. Listen carefully and then answer the question below.

3. How did the author "trick" you about what was going on in the story?

Lesson 7

John Henry

• *Folktale*

Heads Up People often talk about "plot" when watching a movie or television program. You might say or hear something like, "I didn't understand the plot," or "The plot was really exciting." The word *plot* is used to mean "what happens." Stories have plots too. They are based on a series of actions that happen in sequence surrounding a problem that needs to be solved. In "John Henry," the problem has to do with a new machine. Technology can solve many problems, but it can create problems too. In the box below, brainstorm problems that are caused by technology.

As you read the folktale, think about the problem and what happens because of the problem. Respond to the Think-Along Questions. Also, as you read, circle or highlight any words you don't know.

John Henry

retold by Peg Hall

My Thoughts

1   John Henry was born to be a steel-driving man. Why, when he was little more than a boy, John Henry could swing a hammer. He could swing it higher and faster than a grown man could.

2   But there wasn't any steel driving for John Henry. Not at first. He spent his days picking cotton on his master's plantation. He spent his nights listening to the *click-clack* of trains carrying Southern soldiers to battle. And he dreamed about driving steel.

What do you think "driving steel" means?

3   John Henry told his mama and papa about his dreams. "I'm not surprised," said his papa. "It's plain to see that you were born to be a steel-driving man."

4   "There's more," said John Henry. "I dreamed that I'd die with a hammer in my hand."

5   John Henry's words worried his mama and papa. But they knew their boy was safe with them. And after a while they forgot what he had said.

6   However, John Henry never forgot his dream of driving steel. Not even when he got to be full-grown. Not even when he fell in love with sweet Polly Ann.

7   Not even when he made her his bride. And not even when Polly Ann gave him a fine, **strapping** son.

8   Then the Civil War ended. The slaves were free. At last men like John Henry could do what they wanted. John Henry knew what *that* was.

What does "men like John Henry" mean?

continued

John Henry continued

9　　To the west, men were building a great railroad that would cross the country. So John Henry said to his wife, "Polly Ann, we have to go west. For I was born to be a steel-driving man."

10　　John Henry, Polly Ann, and their baby left the very next day. As they walked, John Henry said to himself, "There's a hammer waiting for me somewhere. I just know it."

11　　On the third day of their trip, John Henry and Polly Ann heard something. *Clang-clang. Clang-clang.* It was the sound of hammers against steel.

12　　When they went around the next bend, they saw gangs of men. The men were driving steel spikes into the wooden ties that held the train tracks. One man in each gang knelt by the track, holding a great spike ready. Three others stood by him with hammers in their hands. ONE-TWO-THREE—each took a great swing. And ONE-TWO-THREE—their mighty blows drove the spike into the track. Then the gang moved on to another spot.

13　　John Henry felt his heart beat in time with the blows of the hammers. This was what he was born to do. This was what he would do.

14　　He went to find the foreman. "I'm a steel-driving man," John Henry said. "And I need a job."

15　　The foreman frowned. "A steel-driving man, you say? How long have you been at it?" he asked.

16　　"No time at all," said John Henry. "But I was born knowing how."

17　　The foreman shook his head. "That's not good enough," he said. "Steel driving is hard and dangerous work. I need men who know what they're doing. Not beginners who might hit someone."

> How do you think John Henry will solve this problem?

18   John Henry wasn't about to give up. Not when his dream was right before him. "Let me show you," he said. "I won't hit anyone. Why, I can drive one of those spikes all by myself."

19   That made the foreman laugh. "Now I'm sure you don't know what you're doing," he said. "No one can drive a railroad spike by himself."

20   "I can," said John Henry softly. "Just let me use one of your hammers."

21   Well, by now some of the other men had heard John Henry. They stopped working and poked one another. One of them said, "Go ahead and let him try, boss. We want to see how one man can drive a spike."

22   "Yes," said another. "Let's see for ourselves."

23   "Fine," said the foreman. "If one of you is crazy enough to hold it for him."

24   Now that was a different matter. No one wanted to hold a spike for someone who didn't know what he was doing. So there was some shifting of feet and a lot of whispering.

25   "I'm no fool," said one man.

26   "Nor am I," said another.

27   "I'm no fool either," said a third. "But I'll hold it for him."

continued

John Henry continued

28   The speaker stepped toward the tracks. He was a little man with a head of black, curly hair. He gave John Henry a big grin. The he picked up a spike, bent down, and held it in place.

29   "It's your life, Willie," said the foreman. "But I think you're a fool."

30   John Henry picked up a hammer. He swung it back and forth a few times, just testing it. Then he nodded and stepped over to the spike.

31   Everyone was quiet, even the baby in Polly Ann's arms. Every eye was on John Henry.

> Predict what will happen.

32   John Henry started to swing. The huge hammer flashed through the air. It moved so fast that it was a blur. It moved so fast that Willie felt its wind against his cheek.

33   *CLANG!* The hammer hit the spike in the dead center. Sparks shot out as iron met steel.

34   "Sit back now, Willie!" shouted John Henry. Then—*CLANG!* John Henry swung again.

35   There was a gasp from the crowd. The spike had been driven all the way into the wood!

36   "Tell me your name, son," said the foreman.

37   "I'm John Henry," he said. "And this is my wife Polly Ann and our baby."

38   "Well, you've got yourself a job, John Henry," said the foreman. "And a cabin for you and your family."

39   At last John Henry was a steel-driving man. And the world had never seen anyone work like he did. No one was faster or more powerful. John Henry could work for ten hours without stopping. Why,

before long, he started using a hammer in each hand. Then he could work twice as fast! People would come from all over just to watch.

40   Now the railroad tracks were heading west—right through the mountains. Those mountains were made up of hard rock. And a lot of that rock had to be moved to make way for the tracks.

41   So one of John Henry's jobs was driving steel drills into the rock. The drills would make a hole. Then workers could put black powder into the hole. They'd light the powder and blow the rock to pieces.

42   It took a lot of workers to keep up with John Henry. Why, five men were needed just to carry the steel drills he used up in one day. But only one man ever held the drills in place. That was Willie. He and John Henry were a team.

43   Then one day, a stranger showed up at the railroad camp. He asked for the foreman. He said, "Today is your lucky day, sir. I've got a machine that can help you. My steam drill can do the work of five men. It can make holes in solid rock so fast that your men can't keep up."

44   The foreman looked the salesman up and down. "Don't need it," he said at last.

> Why did the foreman tell the salesman he didn't need the machine?

45   "Of course you need it," said the salesman. "Why, this steam drill is the best machine ever built!"

46   "Don't need it," said the foreman again. "I've got John Henry. The best steel driver ever born. He can outdrill any machine."

continued

John Henry continued

47   "You think so?" said the salesman. "Well, I tell you what. We'll have a contest. A race between my machine and your man."

48   "What's the prize?" asked the foreman.

49   "If your man wins, you get my steam drill for free. If my machine wins, you buy it from me."

50   "Sounds fair to me," said the foreman. "But I have to check with John Henry first."

51   So the foreman sent someone to get John Henry. When the big man arrived, the foreman asked, "How do you feel about racing a steam drill, John Henry?"

52   John Henry looked at the steam drill. Then he looked at the heavy hammer in his hand. He lifted it, feeling the way the muscles bunched in his arms.

53   "Race a machine?" he said. "Why, a machine has no heart. It's nothing but a machine. I'll race it. And I'll beat it. Or I'll die trying."

54   The contest was set for the very next day. Polly Ann and Willie both tried to change John Henry's mind. But nothing they said helped. John Henry was going to race that machine.

> **Why did Polly Ann and Willie try to change John Henry's mind?**

55   The next morning a great crowd gathered where a tunnel was to be drilled. The steam drill was at one side. The machine gleamed in the bright sunshine. The men who ran it were busy. One was adding oil. Another was adding grease. A third was feeding the fire that made the steam and powered the drill.

56   John Henry and Willie stood at the other side. John Henry's bare shoulders gleamed like black coal. His hammer was in his hand.

57   "Are you ready?" shouted the foreman.

58   The steam drill salesman nodded. So did John Henry. Then the starting gun went off. The race began.

59   John Henry raised his hammer high into the air. *CLANG!* It hit the head of the steel drill.

60   At the same time, the steam drill began to roar and hiss. The drill bit into the hard rock, sending small stones flying.

61   John Henry didn't pay any attention to the machine. He just kept swinging. Over and over, he lifted the hammer high. Over and over, he brought it smashing down on the head of the steel drills.

62   On one side, men rushed to tend to the machine. On the other side, they rushed to bring new steel drills for Willie to hold and to pour cold water on John Henry's hammer. He was working so hard that the great hammer was smoking.

63   The steam drill hissed and roared. John Henry's hammer clanged and banged. Clouds of steam rose into the air. Rivers of sweat poured down John Henry's back and arms. At the end of an hour the machine was ahead. "Bring me another hammer, Willie!" shouted John Henry. "I'm just getting started! I'm not even tired yet!"

64   A hammer in each hand, John Henry went back to work. He swung those hammers so fast that no one could see them. All they could see were the sparks made when a hammer hit a spike.

65   Inch by inch, the steam drill made one hole in the mountainside.

66   Inch by inch, John Henry made another.

continued

John Henry continued

67   For a time the machine stayed ahead. Then the drill broke and had to be replaced. So John Henry was ahead.

68   It went on like that all morning and all afternoon. First the drill would be ahead. Then John Henry. Then the drill.

69   "The machine's going to win!" some shouted.

70   "John Henry's going to win!" shouted others.

Who do you think will win?

71   John Henry didn't stop to rest. He just kept swinging. His heart thundered in his chest. A roar filled his ears. The noise of the steam drill, he thought.

72   The sun began to sink in the sky. As the last rays slid behind the mountain, there was the sound of a shot. The race was over!

73   "You won, John Henry!" shouted the railroad foreman. "You beat the machine!"

74   John Henry stood there, leaning on a hammer. He nodded once and then fell to the ground.

75   Willie and Polly Ann both rushed to his side. John Henry opened his eyes and smiled at them. "I was a real steel-driving man, wasn't I?" he said. Then he closed his eyes forever.

76   John Henry's story was told many times after that—the story of how a man with a big heart beat a machine with a big engine.

77   Even today, if you listen closely, you can hear the sound of John Henry's hammer. You can hear it in the *click-clack* of the trains as they head down the tracks.

Make Sense of Words   To better understand an unfamiliar word, you can use context clues to try to figure out the meaning. You can also substitute synonyms or antonyms for the word to further understand a word's meaning. *Synonyms* are words that have the same or nearly the same meanings. *Antonyms* are words that have opposite or nearly opposite meanings.

Find the word **strapping** that is bolded in paragraph 7 of "John Henry." Think about the size of John Henry and the preceding word, *fine*. Then complete the chart below.

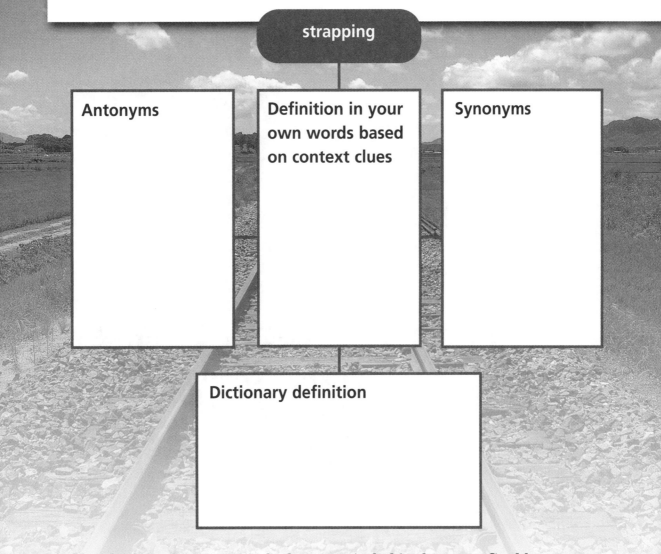

strapping

Antonyms

Definition in your own words based on context clues

Synonyms

Dictionary definition

Now look back at any words that you circled in the story. Could you use any of these techniques to figure out what those words mean?

Read With Understanding Which of the following sentences states the main problem in "John Henry"? Choose the best answer.

① John Henry had to pick cotton on his master's plantation.

② No one wanted to hold the spike for John Henry.

③ John Henry wanted to show that he could beat a machine in a race.

④ It took a lot of workers to keep up with John Henry.

Understand by Seeing It Now based on what you chose as the main problem of the story, fill in the chart below. When completed, the chart will be a summary of the *plot* of "John Henry."

Somebody . . .

Wanted . . .

But . . .

So . . .

Lesson 8

Belle Boyd the Spy

• *Short Story*

Heads Up The *plot* of a story includes not only the problem, but also the events that lead up to the problem and on to the solution. Based on the title of this story and the fact that it comes from a book titled *Tales of the Civil War*, predict what the story will be about by filling in the story frame on the next page.

continued

Belle Boyd the Spy

The story takes place _____

_____.

_____ is a character in the story who _____

_____.

A problem occurs when _____

_____.

After that, _____

and _____.

The problem is solved when _____

_____.

The story ends with _____

_____.

As you read this short story, respond to the Think-Along Questions to help you focus on the *plot*. Also, as you read, circle or highlight any words you don't know.

Belle Boyd the Spy

retold by Peg Hall

1   During and after the War Between the States, tales were told of brave deeds. There were heroes on both sides of the fight. They were Northerners and Southerners, men and women.

2   This is the tale of a brave woman of the South. Her name was Belle Boyd.

3   The story begins when Belle was just a girl. The Union army had taken over the town where she lived. Belle's father was away fighting for the South. Belle and her mother had been left to keep their home safe.

4   One morning Belle was upstairs. She heard her mother give a frightened cry. At once Belle grabbed a gun from under her bed. Her father had given it to her before he left. She hid it under her long skirt and flew downstairs.

Why do you think Belle's father had given her a gun?

5   There, she found her mother fighting off a Union soldier.

6   "Tell me where your Confederate flag is hidden!" the soldier cried.

7   Belle's mother told him they had no flag. But the soldier wouldn't listen. There was talk in town, he said. Talk that the Boyds were hiding a Confederate flag. And now that the Union army had taken over, that was against the law.

8   Again Mrs. Boyd said there was no flag. But the angry soldier pushed her against the wall.

9   "Let her go!" cried Belle.

continued

Belle Boyd the Spy continued

10   The soldier turned and smiled at her. He saw a
young girl—nothing to fear. So he moved closer to
Mrs. Boyd. He put one hand around the woman's
thin arm.

11   "Didn't you hear me?" asked Belle in a low voice.

12   "Be quiet!" snapped the soldier. "Pretty as you
are, I'd sure hate to have to hurt you. And I might
have to."

13   He headed for the door. And he was pulling
Belle's mother along with him!

Predict what will happen.

14   That was all Belle needed to see. She took the
gun out from under her dress.

15   Belle called out one more warning. But the Union
soldier kept moving.

16   Belle lifted the gun in her shaking hands. Then
she fired. The soldier dropped to the floor.

17   "He's dead!" cried Mrs. Boyd. "Oh, Belle, what
have you done? What will happen to us now?"

18   "I don't know, Mother," said Belle. "I just know
that we can't give up our flag. I have a strange
feeling about it. I think that if we lose that flag, the
South will lose the war."

19   The next day Belle was brought before a captain
in the Union army. "This is a serious charge, Miss
Boyd," the captain said. "I could send you to
prison. So tell me, why did you kill that soldier?"

20   Belle kept her eyes on the floor. In a small voice,
she told her story. She explained that the soldier
had been hurting her mother.

**Why did Belle speak in a small voice and keep
her eyes on the floor?**

© **Perfection Learning®** No reproduction permitted.

21 The Union captain studied the girl standing in front of him. She seemed small and helpless. Not at all dangerous.

22 The captain shook his head. He was a good man who hated war and loved his own mother. So he could understand what Belle had done.

23 The captain reached into his desk drawer. He pulled out a small gun. "Here," he said. "You may need to protect your mother and yourself again. Next time, use this. But don't kill any more of my soldiers. Not unless they are trying to hurt you. I'd not like to see this war won by a girl."

24 Belle's lips smiled as she took the gun. But her eyes were angry.

25 Two years later the town was still under Union control. Belle was used to seeing soldiers on the streets and in the shops. And they were used to seeing Belle.

26 The soldiers never saw anything to worry about in Belle. She was just a pretty girl who lived in town.

27 But Belle kept her eyes and ears open. She became a spy for the South.

28 It happened for the first time when some Union officers met in a hotel. Belle was there too, in a room above. She lay with her ear against the floor, listening.

29 Belle heard loud voices and laughter. Then a door slammed, and Belle's heart beat faster. What if they found her? she thought. She would be shot as a spy!

continued

Belle Boyd the Spy continued

30   Still, she kept on listening. For a time, nothing important was said. But then she heard the voice of General Banks, a Union leader.

31   "Here," he said. "Look at the map. This is where Stonewall Jackson and his army will be. I will lead my men to a spot in front of Jackson. The rest of you will have him trapped in a pocket."

32   Belle held her breath and listened. At last she heard the general tell where and when the trap would be set. She knew what she had to do.

What do you think Belle will do?

33   Belle went to work. She wrote letters to General Banks and each of his men. The letters invited them to a party.

34   Belle delivered the letters. Then she hurried from the hotel. She found a fast horse and headed for the mountains. She knew that was where General Stonewall Jackson was camped.

35   It was a dark, windy night. At first Belle was frightened. There was no one else out. It was against the law to be outside after dark without a special **pass**. And passes were hard to get.

36   Belle had a pass. But it wasn't really hers. If anyone checked it, he or she would know. And then that person would know that she was a spy. And if that happened, Belle would be killed. For that was the fate of any spy.

37   Still, Belle went on. She had to get to Stonewall Jackson and back before daylight.

38   Suddenly, she heard a shout. "Halt! Who goes there?"

39   It was a Union soldier!

40   Belle pulled the horse to a stop. "I have a pass," she said in a shaking voice. "My aunt is sick. I'm just going to visit her."

41   Slowly, she reached into her pocket. But the soldier didn't wait to see her pass. He just waved her on. After all, she was just a girl. She couldn't be dangerous.

> Why did the soldier think girls couldn't be dangerous?

42   Before long, Belle reached Jackson's camp. She gave her message then left. The sun was just coming up when she got back to town.

43   The night of the party arrived. Belle was there to greet her guests. She wore a lovely dress—and a warm smile.

> Why do you think Belle is having a party?

44   The Union officers thought Belle smiled because of the party. But she had other reasons for being happy.

45   Soon the music started. All the officers wanted to dance with Belle. And dance she did. She danced as if she hadn't a care in the world.

46   General Banks himself had been watching her. At last he asked her to dance. As the music started up again, they swept out onto the floor.

47   "This is a lovely party, Miss Boyd," the general said. "And you are equally lovely."

48   Belle smiled and said a soft thank-you.

49   "So I guess you can see that Union soldiers aren't all bad," the general said. Belle didn't answer.

continued

Belle Boyd the Spy continued

50   "You Confederate ladies surely know how to put on a party," the general went on. "You are far better at that than your men are at fighting."

51   The general began to laugh. And Belle stopped dancing. She was angry. But she was trying to hide her feelings.

52   "You must excuse me, General," she said with a smile. "I have something I want to give you."

53   Belle left the general in the middle of the dance floor. She hurried from the room.

54   When Belle returned, she had a folded piece of cloth in her arms.

55   "For you, General," said Belle with a laugh. Then she threw the cloth over his head. As it unfolded, everyone could see what it was. A Confederate flag!

56   Suddenly, the door flew open. And in ran the Confederate soldiers! Their guns were drawn and ready to fire.

57   The Union soldiers didn't have guns with them. After all, they were at a party. Some ran off to get their guns. Others ran to get away. All those who ran were killed on the spot.

58   The room was filled with the sounds of shots and screams. Some of the ladies fainted. But others—all Southerners—smiled.

59   At last the room was quiet. The Union men were lined up and marched out of the room.

60   As General Banks passed, Belle smiled.

61   "How is this for being caught in a pocket, General?" she asked.

> Where had Belle heard those words before?

62   The general stared at Belle in surprise. He could hardly believe she was using the very words he had used. She had set the trap before he could!

63   A few weeks later, Belle Boyd got a note from Stonewall Jackson. In it, he thanked her for her bravery.

64   For the rest of the war, Belle kept the note in a safe place—right next to her Confederate flag.

My Thoughts

Make Sense of Words Sometimes the same word can have different meanings based on how it is used in a sentence. A word can be used as a *verb* (an action word) or a *noun* (a person, place, or thing). Find the word **pass** in paragraph 35 of the story. Think about how the word is used in the story and then fill in the chart below. You will need to use the dictionary to look up definitions. Remember, a *synonym* is a word with the same or nearly the same meaning.

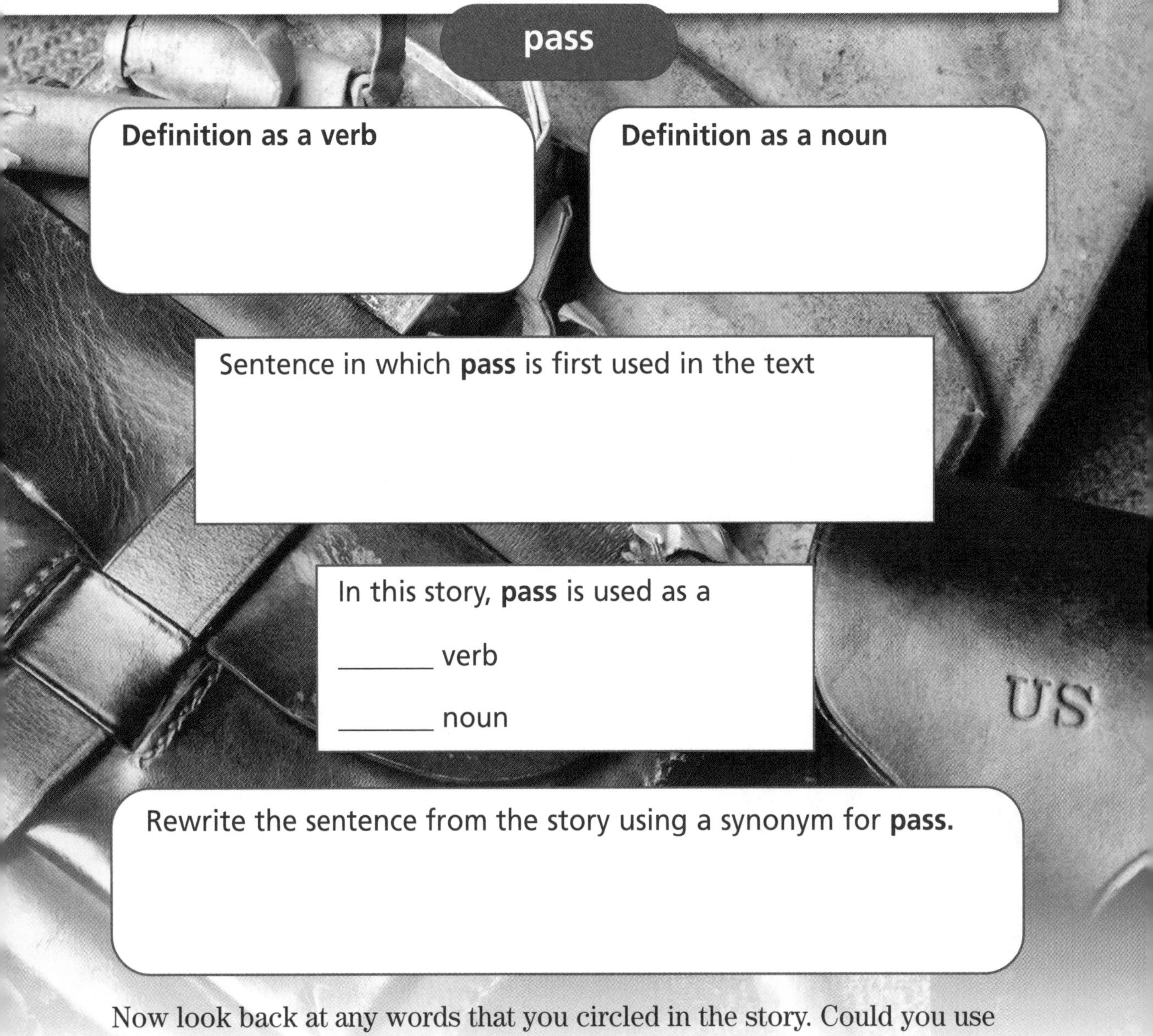

pass

Definition as a verb

Definition as a noun

Sentence in which **pass** is first used in the text

In this story, **pass** is used as a

_____ verb

_____ noun

Rewrite the sentence from the story using a synonym for **pass.**

Now look back at any words that you circled in the story. Could you use any of these techniques to figure out what those words mean?

Read With Understanding Which of the following events did *not* happen in "Belle Boyd the Spy"?

① Belle's father came home from the war.

② The Union captain gave Belle a small gun to protect herself and her mother.

③ Belle killed a Union soldier who had been hurting her mother.

④ Belle threw a party for the Union soldiers.

Understand by Seeing It After Belle heard General Banks describing how they would trap Stonewall Jackson, Belle knew what she had to do. Fill in the blanks below to list the steps of her plan that led to the *climax*, or turning point, of the story.

1. First Belle wrote _____.

2. When a Union soldier stopped Belle, she told him that _____ _____.

3. Belle found a fast horse and _____ _____.

4. When Belle reached Jackson's camp, she _____ _____.

5. The last person Belle danced with at her party was _____ _____.

6. When Belle threw the _____ over the General,

   the door _____.

7. The _____ killed or captured the _____.

8. General Banks was shocked when Belle asked him

   " _____

   _____?"

Write to Learn Pretend that you are Belle Boyd and you are ready to put your plan to capture General Banks into action. Write a note inviting him to a party at your house so that he will be sure to come but will be unaware of what lies in store for him.

Lesson 9

He Was No Bum

• *Article*

Heads Up In this article, the author proves that a first impression can be wrong. He does so by describing the main character in a different way than readers would have originally thought. He *characterizes* the "bum" through

- direct description
- the character's actions
- others' actions toward the character
- what others say about the character

Think of someone you know well. Describe that person on the next page, providing direct description, things that person does, other people's reactions to and actions toward that person, and things others say about him or her. Write the person's name in the oval in the middle of the chart.

Direct description

Actions

Others' reactions/actions

What others say

The main character, Arthur Joseph Kelly, never speaks directly in this article. Yet by reading about what happened to him during his life and how others reacted to him, you will get a clear picture of Mr. Kelly. Respond to the Think-Along Questions to help understand why so many people cared about this man. Also, as you read, circle or highlight any words you don't know.

He Was No Bum

by Bob Greene

1   A bum died. That's what it seemed like. They found his body in a **flophouse** on West Madison Street, Chicago's Skid Row. White male, approximately fifty-five years old. A bum died.

2   They didn't know.

3   He was no bum. And his story . . . well, let his story tell itself.

4   The man's name was Arthur Joseph Kelly. Growing up, he wanted to be a fireman. When he was a child he would go to the firehouse at Aberdeen and Washington, the home of Engine 34. His two sisters would go with him sometimes. The firemen were nice to the kids. This was back in the days when the neighborhood was all right.

What is the author saying about the neighborhood now?

5   Arthur Joseph Kelly became a teenager, and then a man, and he never quite had what it takes to be a fireman. He didn't make it. He did make it into the Army. He was a private in World War II, serving in the European Theater of Operations. He didn't make out too well. He suffered from shell shock. It messed him up pretty badly.

6   He was placed in a series of military hospitals, and then, when the war was over, in veterans' hospitals. Whatever had happened to him in the service wasn't getting any better. He would be released from a hospital, and he would go back to the old neighborhood in Chicago, and suddenly the L train would come rumbling overhead and Arthur

Joseph Kelly would dive to the ground. Some people laughed at him. He didn't want to do it. A loud noise and he would drop.

> Why would he drop to the ground when he heard a loud noise?

7   He walked away from a veterans' hospital in 1954. He decided that he had to live in the real world. But he was in no condition to do that. He tried for a while, and then he went back to the only place that he remembered as being a place of happiness.

8   He went back to the fire station at Aberdeen and Washington.

9   Some of the men of Engine 34 remembered Arthur Joseph Kelly from when he was a boy. They remembered him as a bright-eyed child wanting to be a fireman. And now they saw him as a shell-shocked war veteran.

> How do you think the firemen treated Kelly?

10   They took him in.

11   They fed and clothed him and gave him a place to sleep and let him be one of them. He wasn't a fireman, of course, but he lived in the firehouse, and he had the firemen as his friends. The military people didn't know what to do with his veterans benefits, so some of the firemen went to the Exchange National Bank and arranged for the benefit money to be paid to a special account. The firemen of Engine 34 took it upon themselves to become Arthur Joseph Kelly's conservator and **guardian.**

continued

He Was No Bum continued

12   The years went by. Some of the firemen were transferred, and some retired, and some died. But there was always at least one fireman at the station who would take responsibility for Arthur Joseph Kelly. The fireman didn't ask for anything in return, but Kelly would stoke the furnace and clean up and help out as much as he could. There were maybe a dozen firemen over the years who became his special **guardians**—the ones who would deal with the bank and the military, and who would make sure that no harm came to Kelly. For a long time it was the Sullivan brothers; when they left Engine 34, another fireman willingly took over, and then another.

> Why do you think Kelly worked around the firehouse even though he didn't have to?

13   Once Arthur Joseph Kelly went to a Cubs game. A car backfired. He hit the ground. There was some snickering. But an older man, who had been in the service himself and was familiar with shell shock, helped Kelly up and said, "That's all right, fellow. You'll be all right." After that, Kelly stayed close to the firehouse.

14   His mind and his nerves were not good. The firemen had to remind him to bathe, and to change clothes, and to eat properly. They did it, for twenty years and more, without anyone asking. "He's an easygoing fellow," one of them said. "He doesn't harm anybody. It's not so hard for us to take care of him."

15   Then the firehouse closed down. The firemen were transferred to another station house, at Laflin

and Madison. Arthur Joseph Kelly went with them, but it wasn't the same. It wasn't the firehouse he had loved as a child. He didn't want to live there.

Why do you think the move affected Kelly so much?

16   So the last fireman to take care of him—George Grant, a fifty-one-year-old father of eight—found Arthur Joseph Kelly a place to live. It wasn't much—it was the room on Madison Street—but every month Grant would take care of the financial arrangements with the bank, and would go to Madison Street to give money to a lady who ran a tavern near Kelly's room. The understanding was that she would give Kelly his meals at the tavern. No liquor. The firemen didn't want Kelly to end up as a Madison Street wino.

17   "The firemen had started taking care of Art way before I even got on the force," Grant said. "I just happened to be the last in a long line of men who took care of him. I didn't mind."

18   When Arthur Joseph Kelly was found dead in his room, they thought he was a bum. But they should have been at the funeral.

19   Arthur Joseph Kelly was buried with dignity. He was carried to his grave by uniformed firemen. They were his pallbearers. Most of them were not even born when, as a boy, Kelly had started hanging around the firehouse. But they were there at the end. The firemen never let Kelly live like a bum. They didn't let him die like one, either.

How did his funeral show that Kelly wasn't a bum?

Make Sense of Words

1. Context clues can help you figure out the meaning of some unfamiliar words. Look at the word **flophouse** in the first paragraph of the article. Reread the sentence it is in. After reading the rest of the article and seeing what kind of a life Arthur Joseph Kelly led, which is most likely the definition of **flophouse**?

    (A) mansion

    (B) jail

    (C) cheap rooming house

    (D) executive business suite

2. Sometimes when you come across an unfamiliar word, it will be explained further in the text. Find the word **guardian** in paragraph 11. Read on to the next paragraph where you will see the word again, in the plural form, **guardians**. In this paragraph, the author has given you examples of what a **guardian** does. Fill in the chart below to show that you understand what the word means.

guardian

> Examples from text of what a **guardian** does
>
> Fireman became kelly's guardian

> Definition in your own words
>
> a person who cares for persons or property

Now look back at any words that you circled in the story. Could you use any of these techniques to figure out what those words mean?

Read With Understanding

Authors can reveal *characterization* several ways. Sometimes the character speaks to the reader directly. Sometimes the author describes the character and/or tells what the character does. Sometimes, however, a character is revealed through the way other people in the story react to him or her.

From the following statements, choose the best reason that shows why Arthur Joseph Kelly was *not* a bum.

① Arthur Joseph Kelly always wanted to be a fireman.

② Arthur Joseph Kelly was a private in World War II.

③ The firemen of Engine 34 always wanted to take care of Arthur Joseph Kelly.

④ Arthur Joseph Kelly always remembered the home of Engine 34 as a place of happiness.

Some people may have thought that Arthur Joseph Kelly was a poor man who died alone, but his life did have meaning because of the people who cared about him, his dreams, and what he did for his country. Fill in the chart below to show your understanding of his character.

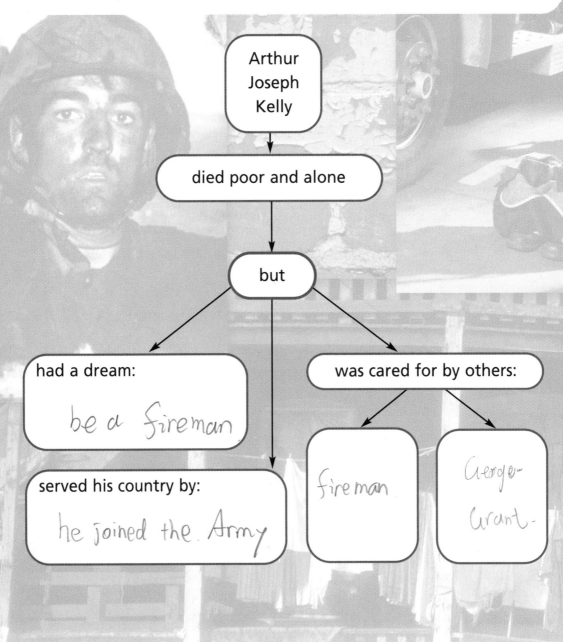

Arthur Joseph Kelly

died poor and alone

but

had a dream:

be a fireman

served his country by:

he joined the Army

was cared for by others:

fireman

George Grant.

Write to Learn The firemen who took care of Arthur Joseph Kelly did so because they wanted to. Think about a time in your life when you did something for someone else. Write below about what you did and how this act of kindness made you feel.

Lesson 10

Carlie
from
The Pinballs

• Novel Excerpt

Heads Up Authors let you as a reader know what characters are like by telling you directly, by letting the characters reveal themselves to you by what they say and do, and by showing how other characters react to them. In "Carlie," which is an excerpt from the novel *The Pinballs*, the author introduces you to three children who are going to live together as part of a foster family. None of these children has met before. On the next page, describe how you would feel if you were placed in such a situation.

How I Would Feel

_____

_____

_____

_____

_____

_____

_____

Even though this is a short selection, you will get a good picture of these children, especially the girl Carlie, both by what the author tells you about them and by what they reveal about themselves through their conversation. As you read this selection, answer the Think-Along Questions, which will help you focus your thinking on understanding *characterization*. Also, as you read, circle or highlight any words you don't know.

Carlie *from* The Pinballs

by Betsy Byars

1   Carlie had been suspicious of people since the day she was born. She swore she could remember being dropped on the floor by the doctor who delivered her.

2   "You weren't dropped," her mother had told her.

3   "All right then, why is my face so flat? Was I *ironed*?"

4   Carlie also claimed that when she was two months old a baby-sitter had stolen a golden cross from around her neck.

5   "No baby-sitter stole a gold cross from you," her mother had told her.

6   "All right then, where is it?"

> Do you think Carlie can remember these things? Explain.

7   Carlie believed everyone was out to do her in, and she had disliked Mrs. Mason, the foster mother, as soon as she had seen her standing in the doorway.

8   "I knew she'd have on an apron," Carlie said to the social worker. "She's trying to copy herself after Mrs. Walton—unsuccessfully, I might add."

9   "Maybe she had on the apron because she was cooking, Carlie."

10   "*I* should be the social worker. I'm not fooled by things like aprons."

> Why is Carlie distrustful of Mrs. Mason's apron?

11   She also didn't like the Masons' living room. "This is right out of 'Leave it to Beaver,' " she said.

She especially distrusted the row of photographs over the fireplace. Seventeen pictures of—Carlie guessed—seventeen foster children.

12   "Well, my picture's not going up there," she grumbled to herself. "And nobody better snap me when I'm not looking either." She sat.

13   Mrs. Mason waited until "Young and the Restless" was over and then said, "Carlie?"

14   "I'm still here."

15   "Well, come on and have some lunch. Then afterward you can help me get the boys' room ready."

16   Carlie turned. She looked interested for the first time. "The boys?" she asked. "There're going to be some boys here?"

17   "Yes, two boys are coming this afternoon— Thomas J and Harvey."

18   "How old?"

19   "Eight and thirteen."

20   "Oh, boo, too young." Carlie got up from the footstool. "What's wrong with them?"

21   "Wrong with them?"

22   "Yeah, why do they have to be here? I'm here because I got a bum stepfather. What's their trouble?"

23   "Well, I guess they'll have to tell you that."

24   Carlie lifted her hair up off her neck. "How about the thirteen-year-old?" she asked. "What's he like? Big for his age, I hope."

25   "He has two broken legs. That's about all I can tell you.

26   "Well," Carlie said, "that lets out dancing."

How would you describe Carlie so far?

continued

Carlie from The Pinballs continued

27 Carlie was sitting in front of the television when Harvey arrived. He had to be carried in because of his legs. They set the wheelchair down by Carlie's footstool.

28 She looked around. "What happened to your legs?" she asked. She was interested in medical matters.

29 He said, "Nothing."

30 "Well, *something* must have happened. They don't just put casts on your legs for the fun of it. In fact they *won't* put casts on your legs unless you've had a real accident. I know, because a friend of mine tried to get a cast put on her ankle so she wouldn't have to be in Junior Olympics, and they wouldn't do it." She waited, then she said, "So what happened?"

31 There was a long pause. Harvey looked down at his legs. In his mind the shiny Grand Am lunged over him again. He felt sick. He said, "If you must know, I broke my legs playing football."

32 He wished it had happened that way. A boy at school had broken his ankle playing football, and everyone in school had autographed his cast. Girls had even kissed the cast and left their lipstick prints.

33 Harvey's casts were as white as snow. He wished he had thought to forge some names on them. "Love and kisses from Linda." "Best wishes to a wonderful English student from Miss Howell."

Why do you think Harvey didn't have any names on his cast?

© **Perfection Learning® No reproduction permitted.**

34   Carlie was still looking at him, eyeing the casts, his toes sticking out the end. Then she glanced up at his face.

35   "What position were you playing?"

36   Harvey hesitated. "Quarterback," he said.

37   Carlie snorted. "You're no quarterback. I've seen Joe Namath in person." She looked him over. "If you were playing football at all, you were probably the ball."

38   Harvey kept looking at his legs.

39   Carlie decided to give him one more chance. "So what really happened?"

40   "I was playing football," he insisted.

41   "Listen," Carlie said. "This is one of my favorite shows, so if you're going to tell me a bunch of big lies about what happened to your legs, well, I'll just go back to watching my show."

42   "Go back to watching it," Harvey said.

> **What do you think really happened to Harvey's legs?**

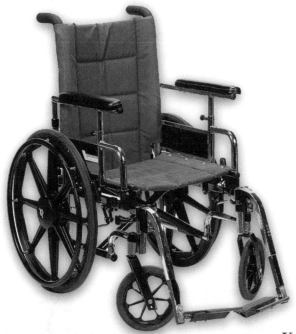

Make Sense of Words Sometimes a word that you usually mean to apply to just one instance can be expanded to become a more far-reaching description of someone's personality. Carlie is described as being "**suspicious** of people since the day she was born." Fill in the chart below to analyze the word **suspicious** and to gain more understanding of Carlie's character.

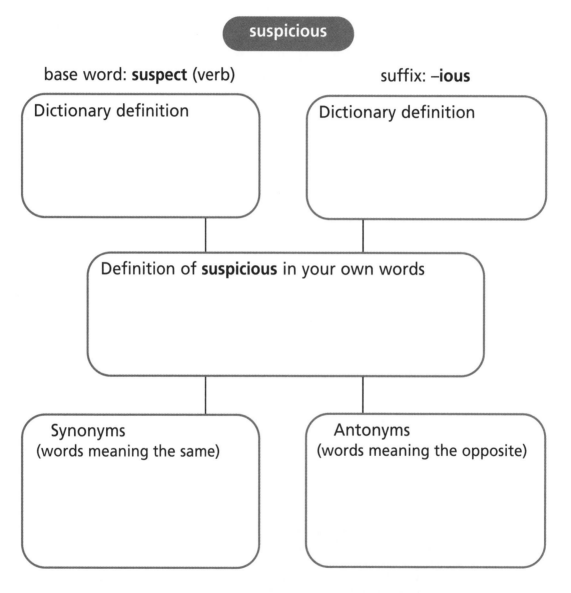

suspicious

base word: **suspect** (verb)   suffix: **–ious**

Dictionary definition

Dictionary definition

Definition of **suspicious** in your own words

Synonyms
(words meaning the same)

Antonyms
(words meaning the opposite)

Now look back at any words that you circled in the story. Could you use any of these techniques to figure out what those words mean?

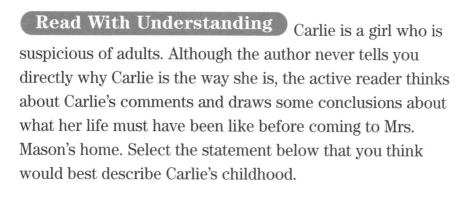

Read With Understanding Carlie is a girl who is suspicious of adults. Although the author never tells you directly why Carlie is the way she is, the active reader thinks about Carlie's comments and draws some conclusions about what her life must have been like before coming to Mrs. Mason's home. Select the statement below that you think would best describe Carlie's childhood.

① The adults in Carlie's life kept abandoning her.

② Carlie had been in many loving foster families.

③ A car had hit Carlie at a young age.

④ A loving, caring stepfather had raised Carlie.

Understand by Seeing It Think about Carlie's personality and the comments she makes as she moves into her new foster home. Then look at the list of adjectives, or describing words, listed below. Five of these fit the character of Carlie, while five do not. Write the words that describe Carlie on the lines surrounding her name. Check the dictionary if there are any words you don't know.

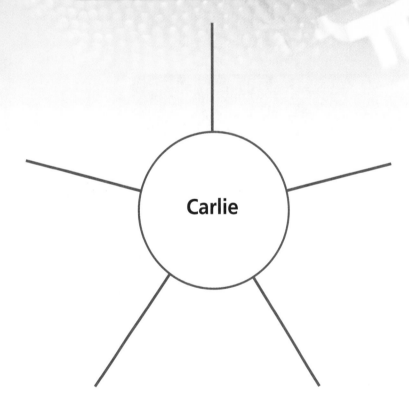

trusting	kind
curious	stubborn
sweet	sarcastic
suspicious	ordinary
troubled	pleasing

Carlie

Write to Learn Another character introduced in "Carlie" is the foster mother, Mrs. Mason, who has 17 pictures of former foster children on the mantel over the fireplace. Do you think she will be able to pull these three new children together into a family? In a paragraph below, predict what you think will happen in the next few months.

Lesson 11

Elephants Are Different to Different People

• *Poem*

Heads Up Sometimes an author presents a major idea about life through a story or poem. Usually this overall "message" is not stated directly. Instead, active readers have to put the ideas and events together to come up with the *theme* the author is trying to express. The *theme* is not the same as the subject, which is what or who the story or poem is about. The theme is the general message that you as the reader can apply to your own life.

Read the statements on the next page. Four are possible themes for a story, while one is a description of the subject. Circle the one you think is the *subject* statement.

Solving family problems takes love and compromise.

It takes bravery to be true to your own beliefs.

This story is about a very smart deer mouse.

Through nature, we learn a lot about the world and ourselves.

Hard lessons and decisions sometimes test friendships.

You are about to read a poem called "Elephants Are Different to Different People" by Carl Sandburg. The subject of the poem is an elephant, but that is not the *theme* of this poem. As you read, respond to the Think-Along Questions, which will help you determine what Sandburg wants to say about life. Also, as you read, circle or highlight any words you don't know.

Elephants Are Different to Different People

by Carl Sandburg

1 Wilson and Pilcer and Snack stood before the
2 zoo elephant.

3 Wilson said, "What is its name? Is it from Asia or
4 Africa? Who feeds it? Is it a he or a she? How old is
5 it? Do they have twins? How much does it cost to
6 feed? How much does it weigh? If it dies how much
7 will another one cost? If it dies what will they use
8 the bones, the fat, and the hide for? What use is it
9 besides to look at?"

What kinds of questions does Wilson ask?

10 Pilcer didn't have any questions: he was
11 murmuring to himself, "It's a house by itself, walls
12 and windows, the ears come from tall cornfields,
13 by God; the architect of those legs was a workman,
14 by God; he stands like a bridge out across deep
15 water; the face is sad and the eyes are kind; I know
16 elephants are good to babies."

How does Pilcer feel about the elephant? How does his reaction differ from Wilson's?

17 Snack looked up and down and at last said to
18 himself, "He's a tough son-of-a-gun outside and I'll
19 bet he's got a strong heart, I'll bet he's strong as a
20 **copper-riveted boiler** inside."

How does Snack's description of the elephant differ from Pilcer's?

21   They didn't put up any arguments.

22   They didn't throw anything in each other's faces.

23   Three men saw the elephant three ways

24   And let it go at that.

25   They didn't spoil a sunny Sunday afternoon;

26   "Sunday comes only once a week," they told

27 each other.

Do you think these men would see other things differently also? Why or why not?

Make Sense of Words Sometimes you may come across a word or phrase that is unfamiliar because it refers to something that is old-fashioned or no longer commonly used. The author may not explain it using *context clues* because he or she assumes you will still be familiar with it. In that case, it is up to you to discover what the unfamiliar word or phrase means. Find the phrase **copper-riveted boiler** that is bolded in the poem. Use your dictionary and the graphic organizer below to help you understand what a **copper-riveted boiler** is.

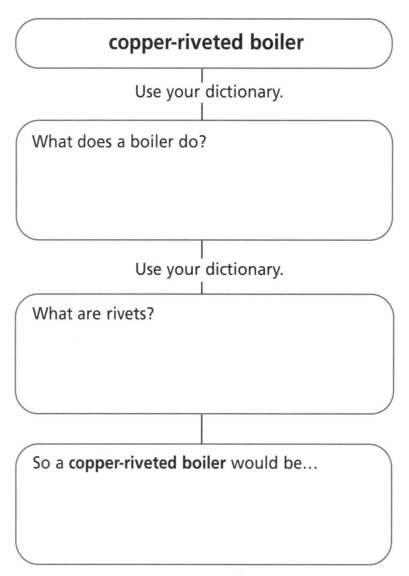

copper-riveted boiler

Use your dictionary.

What does a boiler do?

Use your dictionary.

What are rivets?

So a **copper-riveted boiler** would be...

Now look back at any words that you circled in the poem. Could you use this technique to figure out what those words mean?

Read With Understanding This poem is about three men looking at an elephant and reacting to the huge beast in different ways. The *theme*, however, is more than that. It is the message that you as the reader can apply to your own life. It is implied, or not directly stated.

From the statements below, choose the one that describes a possible *theme* for "Elephants Are Different to Different People."

① Elephants belong in the wild, not in a zoo.

② Going to the zoo is a good way to spend a Sunday afternoon.

③ There should be room in life for different viewpoints.

④ Science is more worthwhile than art.

Understand by Seeing It Think about what you have learned about *theme*. State the theme of "Elephants Are Different to Different People" in your own words in "The author's message" box below. Then think about the information provided in the poem that pointed you to the author's message. Write an example inside each box. One has been provided for you.

The men didn't argue.

The author's message

Write to Learn Do you agree with the author's *theme*? Write a paragraph explaining whether or not you agree and why.

Lesson 12

The Myth of
Pyramus
and Thisbe

- *Myth*

Heads Up In the introduction to "The Myth of Pyramus and Thisbe," you are told that this myth is thought to have been the basis for one of the most famous love stories of all time. What do you know about the story of Romeo and Juliet? Do you know why these two famous lovers were unable to be united? Write what you know about them and the story in the web on the next page.

Romeo
and Juliet

As you read the story of Pyramus and Thisbe, think about what the *theme* of the story is. Remember that the *theme* is the message in the story that you can apply to your own life. Answer the Think-Along Questions as you read. Also, as you read, circle or highlight any words you don't know.

The Myth of
Pyramus and Thisbe

retold by Paula J. Reece

1   *Fate brings two lovers together and forces them to desperate actions. This myth is thought to have been the basis for one of the most famous love stories of all time—Romeo and Juliet.*

2   Pyramus was the handsomest young man in Babylonia. And Thisbe was the fairest maiden. Their parents lived in adjoining houses, and Pyramus and Thisbe fell in love.

3   Pyramus and Thisbe wanted to get married, but their parents wouldn't allow it. Their families didn't get along.

Why do you think the families didn't get along?

4   But the parents couldn't stop Pyramus and Thisbe from loving each other. They communicated through signs and glances. The fire in their hearts burned more intensely from being covered up.

5   It so happened that there was a crack in the wall that separated the two properties. No one had noticed it before. But the lovers discovered it. Through this crack the lovers could talk. They sent tender messages to each other.

6   "Cruel wall," they said. Pyramus was on one side and Thisbe on the other. "Why do you keep two lovers apart? But we are not ungrateful. We know that because of you, we can speak our loving words to each other."

7   They uttered such words on different sides of the wall. And when night came and they had to say good-bye, they pressed their lips upon the wall. They could come no nearer to each other.

8   One morning, they met at their usual spot.

9   "Oh, dear Thisbe," said Pyramus through the crack in the wall, "why do we have such a cruel fate that allows us to hear but not see each other?"

What is "a cruel fate"?

10   "I don't know," answered Thisbe. "If only we could find a way to meet."

11   "Well, why don't we?" asked Pyramus.

12   "But how?" asked Thisbe. "Our parents have forbidden us to see each other."

13   "They won't have to know," said Pyramus. "Tonight when everyone's asleep, we'll slip away."

14   "Where will we go?" asked Thisbe.

15   "We'll leave our houses and walk into the fields," said Pyramus.

16   "Where will we meet?" asked Thisbe.

17   "We will meet at the Tomb of Ninus, right outside the city limits," said Pyramus. "Whoever gets there first will wait for the other at the foot of a certain tree."

18   "I think I know the one," said Thisbe. "The white mulberry tree? The one by the fountain?"

19   "That's the one," answered Pyramus.

Do you think this is a good idea? Why or why not?

20   So Pyramus and Thisbe waited impatiently throughout the day for the sun to go down and for the moon to rise. Finally, night arrived. The families retired to bed.

continued

The Myth of Pyramus and Thisbe continued

21 Thisbe carefully sneaked out of her house. She wore a veil over her head. She rushed to the monument in the fields.

Why do you think Thisbe wore a veil?

22 Sitting under the tree, Thisbe looked around. Suddenly, in the dim light of the moon, she saw a lion. Its jaws dripped blood, and it was approaching the fountain to quench its thirst.

23 Thisbe fled. She found a safe place to hide behind a large rock. But as she was running to the rock, she dropped her veil. After the lion drank from the fountain, it turned to retreat to the woods. That's when it saw the veil. The lion tossed and ripped it with its bloody mouth.

24 Pyramus had been running late. His family hadn't gone to bed as early as he had hoped. Presently he approached the meeting place.

25 The color washed from his cheeks. For he saw in the sand the footsteps of the lion. Then he spied the ripped, bloody veil. He naturally thought Thisbe had been killed by the lion.

26 "Oh, beautiful girl," cried Pyramus, "I have been the cause of your death! You, who are more worthy of life than I, have fallen the first victim. I will follow. I tempted you to a place of such great danger. And I wasn't here first to guard you. Come forth, lion, from the rocks, and tear this guilty body with your teeth!"

Why did Pyramus say he was the cause of Thisbe's death?

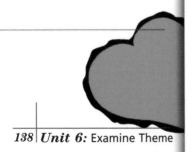

27   Then Pyramus took the veil and carried it with him to the mulberry tree. There he covered the veil with kisses and with tears.

28   "My blood shall also stain you," he said to the veil. He drew out his sword and plunged it into his heart. Pyramus's blood stained all the white mulberries of the tree red.

29   All this time Thisbe had still been hiding behind the rock. But at this time she emerged. She was certain the lion had gone, and she didn't want to disappoint her lover.

30   Thisbe looked around eagerly for Pyramus. She wanted to tell him of the danger she had escaped. She approached the tree. Then she stopped.

31   "Surely this is not the same place," she said to herself. "For the mulberries were white, and these are red. Did I lose my way after hiding?"

32   While she was thinking, she looked around. That's when she saw the body of Pyramus. He was still struggling with death.

33   A shudder ran through Thisbe as the ripple on still water when a sudden breeze sweeps over it. Then she screamed and ran to her lover. She embraced his body. She poured tears into his wounds and pressed kisses on his cold lips.

34   "Oh, Pyramus," she cried. "What has done this? Answer me, Pyramus. It is your own Thisbe who speaks. Hear me, dearest, and lift that drooping head!"

continued

The Myth of Pyramus and Thisbe continued

35   At the name of Thisbe, Pyramus opened his eyes. Then he closed them again.

Predict what Thisbe will do.

36   Thisbe saw her veil stained with blood. Then she saw the **scabbard** empty of its sword.

37   "Your own hand has killed you and because of me," she said. "I, too, can be brave. And my love is as strong as yours. I will follow you in death. For I have been the cause. And death, which alone could part us, will not prevent my joining you. And you, unhappy parents of us both, cannot deny us our united request. As love and death have joined us, let one tomb contain us. And you, tree, don't lose the marks of slaughter. Let your berries still serve as memorials of our blood."

38   Saying this, she plunged the sword into her chest.

39   When their parents found them, they figured out what had happened. They realized that their stubbornness had been at fault. So they granted Thisbe's wish and buried the two lovers together.

What lesson did the families learn?

40   The gods also granted her wish. Forever after, the mulberry tree brought forth red berries. And it still does to this day.

Make Sense of Words Sometimes as you read, you will come across a word that is not defined but because of the way it's used in the sentence and the words that surround it (*context clues*), you can figure out what it means. Look at the word **scabbard**, which is bolded in paragraph 36. Fill in the chart below to show your understanding of what this word means.

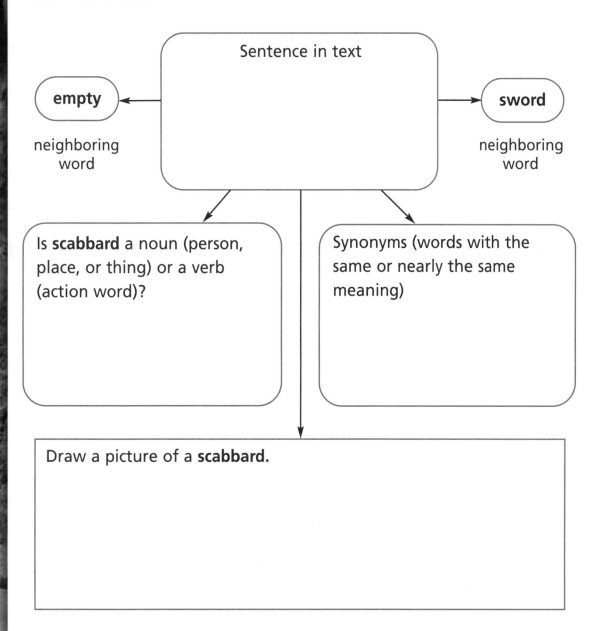

Now look back at any words that you circled in the story. Could you use this technique to figure out what those words mean?

Read With Understanding The story of Pyramus and Thisbe has survived for generations because the message it gives about life relates to people today as much as to those who lived hundreds or even thousands of years ago. Choose the statement below that best expresses a *theme* for this story.

① Parents know best about whom their children should marry.

② Hate among people can cause terrible things to happen.

③ Young people should not be running about at night.

④ Mulberry trees are beautiful because of their red berries.

Understand by Seeing It One way to help determine the theme of a story is to look for *symbols* that an author has chosen to use. A symbol is a concrete object that can stand for a more abstract idea. The American flag is an example because it is a symbol for the country. You don't pledge your allegiance to a piece of cloth but instead to the ideals of the United States. In the story of Pyramus and Thisbe, there are two main symbols that contribute to your understanding of the *theme*. Fill in the chart below to show your understanding of what these symbols stand for.

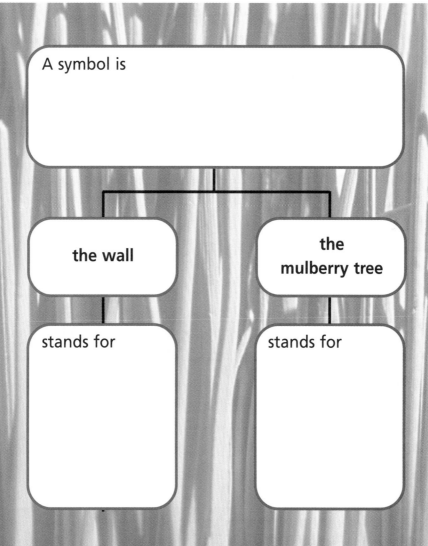

A symbol is

the wall

stands for

the mulberry tree

stands for

Write to Learn What if Thisbe had not dropped her veil? How would the story be different? Do you think that the story would have the same *theme*? Rewrite the ending, and then write a sentence for the new (or same) theme.

New ending

_____

_____

_____

_____

_____

_____

_____

_____

_____

_____

_____

Theme

_____

_____

_____

The Lady, or the Tiger?

• *Short Story*

Heads Up The story of "The Lady, or the Tiger?" needs to be read by an active reader. Take all the strategies you have learned in this section and use them while reading this short story. Focus on the events of the *plot*, the *characters*, and the *theme* of the story. This story is unique because it actually requires the reader to be a participant in the story. Because the theme of this story is based around the question of which is stronger, love or jealousy, put yourself in the following situation:

Imagine that someone you love is either going to be killed or is going to marry someone you can't stand. Which would you choose for that person?

Write your thoughts on the next page.

My Thoughts

_____

_____

_____

_____

_____

_____

_____

_____

_____

As you read, answer the Think-Along Questions to help focus your
thinking on the reading strategies you have learned.

The Lady, or the Tiger?

by Frank R. Stockton • retold by Paula J. Reece

1   In the very olden time, there lived a king. This spirited king had a cruel streak. He also had some crazy ideas. But his people obeyed him so much that his ideas usually became facts.

2   When everything went smoothly, the king was composed and happy. And whenever there was a little hitch, he was even more composed and happier yet. Nothing pleased him more than to make the crooked straight or to crush down uneven places.

3   One of his borrowed ideas was that of a public arena. The arena displayed manly and beastly bravery. This caused his citizens' minds to be refined and cultured.

> What kind of man is the king?

4   But even here the king showed his enthusiastic and cruel side. He used the huge stadium for true justice. Crime was punished or innocence rewarded by the laws of something fair and flawless—chance.

5   If a citizen was accused of a crime, the king decided if it interested him. If it did, then the public was notified. On a certain day, the fate of the person would be decided in the king's arena.

6   On that day, all the people gathered in the bleachers. The king would be surrounded by his court. He would sit high on his throne on one side of the arena.

continued

The Lady, or the Tiger? continued

7   When the king gave a signal, a door beneath him opened. The accused person stepped out into the arena. Directly across from the accused were two doors. They were exactly alike and side by side. The person on trial had to walk straight to the doors and open one of them.

Predict what are behind the doors.

8   The person could open either door. But he could receive no help or opinions except from chance itself.

9   If the accused opened one door, out came a hungry tiger. It would be the fiercest and cruelest that could be captured. It would immediately spring upon him and tear him to pieces. It was a punishment for his guilt.

10   As soon as the case of the criminal was decided, sad iron bells were clanged in the kingdom. Great cries went up from the hired mourners who were posted on the outer rim of the arena. Then the large audience went slowly home with bowed heads and heavy hearts. They mourned that one so young and fair, or so old and respected, should have deserved such a frightful fate.

11   But if the accused person opened the other door, out came a lady. She was the most suitable to his age and rank that His Majesty could select among his citizens. To this lady the accused was instantly married. It was a reward of his innocence.

12   It didn't matter if he already had a wife and family or if he was already engaged to a woman of his own choosing. The king didn't allow such

arrangements to interfere with his great scheme of punishment and reward.

13   The vows took place right away in the arena. Following the ceremony, merry brass bells rang. The people shouted glad hurrahs. The innocent man, followed by children dropping flowers on his path, led his bride to his home.

14   This was the king's semicruel method of carrying out justice. Its perfect fairness is clear. The criminal opened whichever door he wished. And he never had the slightest idea whether, in the next instant, he would be devoured or married.

15   Sometimes the tiger came out of one door. Sometimes it came out of the other. The decisions were not only fair, they were positively final. The accused person was instantly punished if he found himself guilty. And if innocent, he was rewarded on the spot whether he liked it or not.

What do you think of the king's system of justice?

16   The trials were very popular. Many people gathered. They never knew whether they would witness a bloody slaughter or a cheery wedding. The uncertainty made it more appealing.

17   Now this semicruel king had a daughter. She was as blooming as his most elaborate ideas. And she had a soul as passionate and commanding as his own. She was the apple of her father's eye. He loved her more than anything.

18   One of the king's attendants was a young man. He was a fine man but had a low rank, just like many of the heroes of romance who loved royal maidens.

continued

The Lady, or the Tiger? continued

19   This royal maiden loved her hero. He was more handsome and braver than any other man in the kingdom. She was completely devoted to him.

20   This love affair moved along happily for many months, until one day the king found out about it. He did not hesitate in regard to his duty. The young man was promptly thrown into prison. A day was chosen for his trial in the king's arena.

21   This, of course, was an especially important occasion. Never before had there been such a case. Never before had a citizen dared to love the daughter of a king.

22   The tiger cages of the kingdom were searched for the most savage beast. The fiercest monster would be selected for the arena.

23   All of the young, beautiful maidens in the kingdom were carefully examined by worthy judges. That was so the young man would have a fitting bride just in case fate did not determine for him a different future.

24   Of course, everybody knew that the deed with which the man was charged had been done. He had loved the princess. And neither he, she, nor anyone else thought of denying it.

25   But the king would not allow any fact of this kind to interfere with the workings of his court of judgment, especially when he took such delight in it. No matter how it turned out, the young man would be out of his daughter's life. And the king would enjoy watching the turn of events. Those

events would determine whether the young man had done wrong in loving the princess.

> **What do you think will be the effect of the king's cruel method of judgment?**

26   The appointed day arrived. People crowded the bleachers of the arena. Those unable to get in massed themselves against its outside walls. The king and his court were in their places, opposite the fateful twin doors.

27   All was ready. The signal was given. A door beneath the king opened. The lover of the princess walked into the arena. He was tall and beautiful.

28   A low hum sounded throughout the crowd. Most of the audience had not known that so grand a young man lived among them. No wonder the princess loved him! What a terrible thing for him to be there!

29   The young man went farther into the arena. Then he turned to bow to the king. It was the custom. But the young man was not thinking at all of the king. His eyes were fixed upon the princess. She sat to the right of her father.

30   From the moment she heard about her lover's trial, the princess had thought of nothing else, night or day. She had more power, influence, and forcefulness than anyone who had ever before been interested in such a case. So she did what no other person had done—she found out the secret of the doors. She knew behind which door waited the tiger. And she knew behind which door stood the lady.

continued

The Lady, or the Tiger? continued

31   The doors were thick with heavy curtains on the inside. So it was impossible that any noise would come from within. Nothing would give a person an idea of what was inside. But gold and the power of a woman's will brought the secret to the princess.

How do you think the princess found out the secret?

32   She not only knew behind which door stood the lady, she also knew who the lady was. She was one of the loveliest damsels of the king's court. She had been selected as the reward of the accused if he was proven innocent of his crime. The princess hated her.

33   The princess had often seen, or imagined she saw, this lovely damsel glancing at her lover. Flirting, she thought. And sometimes the princess thought that her lover had not only noticed, but returned the glances.

34   The princess hated the woman who blushed and trembled behind the silent door.

35   The young man turned and looked at the princess. His eyes met hers. She was paler than anyone in the vast ocean of faces around her. But he could tell by her face that she knew. She knew behind which door crouched the tiger and behind which stood the lady.

36   He had expected her to know it. He understood her nature. He knew that she would never rest until she discovered the secret. The young man's only real chance for success was based on the princess's knowledge.

37   His quick and anxious glance asked, "Which one?" It was as plain to her as if he shouted it from where he stood. There was not an instant to be lost. The question was asked in a flash. It must be answered in another.

38   Her right arm lay on the cushioned armrest. She raised her hand. She made a slight, quick movement to the right. No one but her lover saw her.

39   He turned. Then he quickly walked across the empty space. Every heart stopped beating. Every breath was held. Every eye was fixed on the man. Without hesitating, he went to the door on the right and opened it.

40   Now to the point of the story. Did the tiger come out of that door? Or did the lady?

41   The more we think about this question, the harder it is to answer.

42   Don't think of what you would do. Think of what the **hot-blooded** princess would have done. Despair and jealousy combined to torment her soul. She had lost her lover, but who should then have him?

43   So often had she thought in horror of her lover opening the door behind which waited the cruel fangs of the tiger. But how much more often had she seen him at the other door! In her daydreams she had ground her teeth and torn her hair when she saw his face in ecstasy as he opened the door of the lady!

continued

My Thoughts

44   Her soul had burned in agony when she had seen him rush to meet that woman. When she had heard the glad shouts from the crowd and the wild ringing of the happy bells. When she had seen the priest advance to the couple and make them man and wife before her very eyes!

45   Wouldn't it be better for him to die at once? Then he could wait for the princess in paradise.

46   And yet, that awful tiger! Those shrieks! The blood!

47   Her decision had been shown in an instant. But it had been made after days and nights of terrible consideration. She had known she would be asked. She had decided what she would answer. And without any hesitation, she had moved her hand to the right.

48   The question of her decision is not to be taken lightly. And it is not for me to pretend to be the one with the answer. So I leave it up to all of you. Which came out of the opened door—the lady, or the tiger?

How did the author's ending affect the plot of the story?

Read With Understanding Choose the best answer to each of the following questions about "The Lady, or the Tiger?"

1. Which one of the following statements is true of the king's character?

   Ⓐ The king supported every choice his daughter made.

   Ⓑ The king was only happy when he was in charge of everything.

   Ⓒ The king had a lot of compassion for the victims of his system of justice.

   Ⓓ The king wanted a democratic kingdom where his people helped make decisions.

2. The king felt that his system of justice was fair because

   Ⓐ most of the accused were guilty anyway.

   Ⓑ this way the people could decide who was guilty or innocent.

   Ⓒ it was based on chance.

   Ⓓ the tiger wouldn't really kill anyone.

3. Find the word **hot-blooded** in paragraph 42. Look for context clues surrounding the word. Based on the context clues, what does it mean to be **hot-blooded**?

   Ⓐ to be sick a lot

   Ⓑ to be very loud

   Ⓒ to be easily angered

   Ⓓ to bleed easily

continued

4. Which of the following is a possible theme for this story?

Ⓐ Chance is not always fair.

Ⓑ People should be considered innocent until proven guilty.

Ⓒ Tigers are very dangerous creatures.

Ⓓ A person can never have too much power.

Understand by Seeing It   What do you think? Did the princess tell the young man to choose the door with the lady or the tiger? Think about the reasons that she might have chosen the door with the lady behind it. Then think about the reasons that she might have chosen the door with the tiger behind it. Fill in the chart below to show that you were an active reader as you thought about this story.

Why the <u>tiger</u> is behind the door	Why the <u>lady</u> is behind the door

Write to Learn Which door do you think the young man opened—the one with the tiger or the lady? Write a newspaper article describing the trial. Make sure to include the "5 Ws and the H" of newspaper writing—who, what, when, where, why, and how. Include a headline that will grab your readers' attention.

Out of the Cold

• *Short Story*

Listening comprehension is a valuable skill. Learning and practicing good listening skills will be helpful to you in your life inside and outside of school. When you listen, it is important to focus your attention on the speaker.

Listen as your teacher reads the story "Out of the Cold." Your teacher will stop about halfway through and ask you to make a prediction by answering the first question below.

1. Where do you think this takes place?

_____

After your teacher finishes reading "Out of the Cold," answer the second question below.

2. What was the surprise in the story?

_____

_____

Now your teacher will read "Out of the Cold" again. Listen carefully and then answer the question below.

3. What clues did the author give you about the setting of the story?

Acknowledgments

"Alien Invasion" by Kathryn R. Hoffman. Used with permission from *TIME for Kids* magazine, © 2002.

"Carlie" from *The Pinballs* by Betsy Byars. Copyright © 1977 by Betsy Byars. Used by permission of HarperCollins Publishers.

"Elephants Are Different to Different People" by Carl Sandburg from *The Kingfisher Book of Poetry* © 1985.

"He Was No Bum" reprinted with permission of Scribner, an imprint of Simon & Schuster Adult Publishing Group from *American Beat* by Bob Greene. Copyright © 1983 John Deadline Enterprises, Inc.

"The History of Counting" text copyright © 1997 by Denise Schmandt-Besserat. Used by permission of HarperCollins Publishers.

"Those Three Wishes" from *A Taste for Quiet: And Other Disquieting Tales* by Judith Gorog. Reprinted by permission of the author.

"Three Queens of Egypt" by Vicki León. Copyright © 2002 by National Geographic Society.